CAHSEE Study Guide
Mathematics

Publishing Information

CAHSEE Study Guide Mathematics

© 2008 California Department of Education.

Permission is granted in advance for reproduction of this document for
educational purposes only. The content must remain unchanged and in its
entirety as published by the California Department of Education (CDE). To
request permission to reproduce the information (text or graphics) contained
in this document for resale, submit the specifics of your request in writing to
the Copyright Program Office, California Department of Education, CDE Press,
1430 N Street, Suite 3207, Sacramento, CA 95814. Fax: 916-324-9787.

CALIFORNIA
DEPARTMENT OF
EDUCATION

A MESSAGE TO STUDENTS AND PARENTS

In 1999, California enacted a law requiring that every California public school student pass an examination to receive a high school diploma. The primary purpose of the California High School Exit Examination (CAHSEE) is to significantly improve pupil achievement in public high schools and to ensure that pupils who graduate from public high schools can demonstrate grade level competency in reading, writing, and mathematics. Since 1999 hundreds of thousands of students have taken and passed the CAHSEE. We realize that many students and their families find the prospect of taking this test stressful. Therefore, we are pleased to be able to provide students and their parents with this *Mathematics Study Guide*, which is designed to help students pass the CAHSEE.

The CAHSEE will be administered over two days. On the first day, students will take the English-language arts portion of the test; on the second day, they will take the mathematics portion. All of the questions on the CAHSEE are based on California's academic content standards in English-language arts and mathematics. These standards outline what students are expected to know and be able to do by the end of each school year from kindergarten through high school.

The focus of this study guide is the mathematics part of the exam. It includes questions previously used on the CAHSEE and explains how to determine the correct answers. The guide also gives studying and test-taking tips and answers frequently asked questions. A similar study guide for English-language arts is also available.

Passing the CAHSEE is an achievement for students, and we hope you find this guide helpful. If you have questions or would like more information about the CAHSEE, please contact your high school's principal or your school district's testing office. The California Department of Education's CAHSEE Web site at http://www.cde.ca.gov/ta/tg/hs/ is also an excellent resource.

Good luck with this exam!

Jack O'Connell

CALIFORNIA
DEPARTMENT OF
EDUCATION

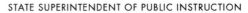

JACK O'CONNELL
STATE SUPERINTENDENT OF PUBLIC INSTRUCTION

UN MENSAJE A LOS ALUMNOS Y SUS PADRES O GUARDIANES

En 1999, el estado de California pasó una ley que exige que todo alumno de una escuela pública de California apruebe un examen para recibir su diploma de preparatoria o *high school*. El propósito del examen es el de asegurar que los alumnos que se gradúen de la preparatoria o *high school* puedan leer y escribir en inglés y puedan usar las matemáticas.

Desde 1999 cientos de miles de estudiantes han tomado y han aprobado el CAHSEE. Nosotros estamos concientes de que el tener que tomar este examen es una fuente de tensión para los alumnos y sus familias. Por eso nos complace proveer a los alumnos y sus padres o guardianes con esta *Guía de Estudio de Matemáticas*, la cual esta diseñada para ayudar a los alumnos a prepararse para pasar el CAHSEE.

El CAHSEE se administra durante dos días. El primer día los alumnos tomarán la sección que se enfoca en los conocimientos de inglés o *English-language arts*. Durante el segundo día los alumnos tomarán la sección del examen que se enfoca en las matemáticas. Todas las preguntas del CAHSEE están basadas en los estándares estatales del contenido de inglés o *English-language arts* y de matemáticas. Estos estándares describen lo que se espera que los alumnos sepan y puedan hacer al final de cada año escolar desde el kinder hasta el 12° grado.

Esta guía de estudio se enfoca en la sección del examen que cubre los conocimientos de **matemáticas**. Incluye preguntas de exámenes previos y provee ayuda para determinar cual es la mejor respuesta; presenta estrategias para estudiar y para responder a preguntas; y responde a las preguntas más frecuentes acerca del examen. Existe una guía similar para la parte del examen que se concentra en inglés o *English-language arts*.

Pasar el CAHSEE es un gran logro para los alumnos y esperamos que esta guía les ayude. Si tiene preguntas o le gustaría obtener más información acerca del examen por favor llame al director de su escuela o a la oficina de evaluación de su distrito escolar. La página de Web del CAHSEE del Departamento de Educación de California también es un recurso excelente. Visítela en: http://www.cde.ca.gov/ta/tg/hs/.

¡Buena suerte con este examen!

NOTE TO READER

We are pleased to present this revised student Study Guide to you. We have made several important changes based on the feedback we received from parents, students, teachers, and administrators. Focus groups from both northern and southern California analyzed the original Student Guides and provided suggestions to make them more useful and accessible to students. The following changes were made to the document:

- We have placed a full practice test in the beginning of the guide with an answer key in the appendix.

- Additional sample test questions have been added to both guides.

- Graphics and page design have been revised to improve readability.

- Mathematics and English-language arts now use consistent strategies to refer to content strands.

- Tabs have been added for easy reference to content strands.

- Explanations to the mathematics practice problems show dual approaches to solve each problem.

- Students are provided with strategies for solving English-language arts questions.

ACKNOWLEDGMENTS

We would like to thank Educational Testing Service (ETS), as well as the staff and students from San Bernardino High School and San Gorgonio High School in San Bernardino and C.K. McClatchy High School in Sacramento for their participation in our focus groups. Additionally, we would like to acknowledge the following CDE staff who provided input to this revised edition:

California Department of Education

Deb V. H. Sigman, Deputy Superintendent
Assessment and Accountability Branch

Tom Herman, Consultant
CAHSEE Office

Janet Chladek, Acting Director
Standards and Assessment Division

Bonnie Galloway, Consultant
CAHSEE Office

Diane Hernandez, Administrator
CAHSEE Office

Carrie Strong-Thompson, Consultant
CAHSEE Office

Much appreciation goes to the educators who contributed to the development of material provided in the original Study Guide.

Principal Author

Jane Hancock, Co-Director
California Writing Project, UCLA

Editor

Carol Jago, Co-Director
California Reading and Literature Project, UCLA
Teacher, Santa Monica High School
Santa Monica High School District

University of California
Office of the President

Elizabeth Stage, Director
Mathematics and Science
Professional Development

Harold Asturias, Deputy Director
Mathematics and Science
Professional Development

Susan Arnold, Assistant to the Director
Mathematics and Science
Professional Development

Advisory Panel

Karen Lopez, Teacher
William S. Hart High School
William S. Hart Union School District

Sidnie Myrick, Associate Director
California Writing Project, UCLA

Cynthia Oei, Teacher
Herbert Hoover High School
Glendale Unified School District

Tylene F. Quizon
Robert A. Millikan High School
Long Beach Unified School District

Anne Gani Sirota, Co-Director
California Reading and Literature Project, UCLA

Joyce Tamanaha-Ho, Teacher
Alhambra High School
Alhambra Unified School District

California Department of Education

Geno Flores, Former Deputy Superintendent
Assessment and Accountability Branch

Deb V.H. Sigman, Director
Standards and Assessment Division

Phil Spears, Former Director
Standards and Assessment Division

Lily Roberts, Former Administrator
CAHSEE Office

Janet Chladek, Former Administrator
CAHSEE Office

Terry Emmett, Administrator
Reading/Language Arts Leadership Office

Jessica Valdez, Consultant
CAHSEE Office

Bruce Little, Consultant
CAHSEE Office

Beth Brenneman, Consultant
Reading/Language Arts Leadership Office

Paul Michelson, Former Consultant
Testing and Reporting Office

Other Contributors

Meg Holmberg, Writing Consultant
EEPS Media

Tim Erickson, Writing Consultant
EEPS Media

Contents

Frequently Asked Questions

The following questions are often asked about the California High School Exit Examination (CAHSEE). If you have a question that is not answered here, call your high school's principal or your school district's testing office. You can find answers to other frequently asked questions on CDE's CAHSEE Web page, http://www.cde.ca.gov/ta/tg/hs/.

What does the CAHSEE cover?

The CAHSEE has two parts: English-language arts and mathematics.

The English-language arts part of the CAHSEE tests state content standards through grade ten. The reading section includes vocabulary, decoding, comprehension, and analysis of informational and literary texts. The writing section covers writing strategies, applications, and the conventions of standard English (for example, grammar, spelling, and punctuation).

The mathematics part of the CAHSEE tests state content standards in grades six and seven and Algebra I. The exam includes statistics, data analysis and probability, number sense, measurement and geometry, mathematical reasoning, and algebra. Students are also asked to demonstrate a strong foundation in computation and arithmetic, including working with decimals, fractions, and percentages.

What kinds of questions are on the CAHSEE?

Most of the questions on the CAHSEE are multiple choice. However, the English-language arts part of the exam also includes one essay question (writing task). The exam is given only in English, and all students must pass the exam in English to receive a high school diploma. Sample questions from previous administrations of the CAHSEE can be found throughout this Study Guide and on CDE's Web site.

When do students first take the CAHSEE?

Students must take the exam for the first time in the second part of their tenth grade year.

When (and how) do students find out whether they have passed the CAHSEE?

School districts receive student score reports about seven weeks after the date of the exam. One copy is to be mailed to the student's home and another copy is to be kept in the student's permanent record. It is important that parents or guardians keep a copy of the student report for their records. The State of California does *not* keep a copy of the scores. All individual student scores are confidential. Only group scores (for entire schools and districts) are made public. Scores may range from 275 to 450. A passing score is 350 or higher.

What if a student does not pass the first time?

Students who do not pass the exam in the tenth grade will have several opportunities to take it again during their junior and senior years. Once they have passed either part of the exam, they will not be tested again on that part. By state law, students who do not pass a part of the exam must be offered extra instruction to learn what they need to know in order to pass. It is up to each school and district to decide how to provide this instruction. To find out what type of help is available and when the exam will be given again at your school, contact the principal or a counselor at your high school.

What if a student is a senior and still has not passed the CAHSEE?

Assembly Bill (AB347) states that you are entitled to receive intensive instruction and services for up to two consecutive academic years after completion of grade 12 or until you have passed both parts of the exit examination, whichever comes first. Also, you have the right to file a complaint regarding those services through the Uniform Complaint Procedure as set forth in California Education Code Section 35186.

What if a student has special needs?

If a student has an individualized education program (IEP) or a Section 504 Plan, it should describe any special arrangements the student is entitled to while taking an exam. Special arrangements for taking the CAHSEE are categorized as either "accommodations" or "modifications." It is important to understand the difference between them because it may affect a student's score on the exam.

An **accommodation** does not alter what the test measures—for example, taking extra breaks during the exam or using a test booklet with large print.

A **modification** fundamentally alters what the exam measures—for example, using a calculator on the mathematics part of the exam or hearing an audio presentation of the questions on the ELA part of the exam.

Students must be permitted to use any accommodations or modifications on the CAHSEE that are specified for testing purposes in their IEP or Section 504 Plan. Students who take the exam using an *accommodation* receive a score just as any other student does. However, students who use a *modification* receive a numeric score followed by the word "MODIFIED." If the student receives a score of 350 or higher, the student may be eligible for a waiver. This is done, in part, by presenting evidence proving that the student has gained the knowledge and skills otherwise needed to pass the CAHSEE.

More information about the procedure for requesting a waiver, including a list of modifications and accommodations, can be accessed on CDE's CAHSEE Web site or by talking with a high school principal.

What if a student is still learning to speak and read in English?

All students must pass the CAHSEE to be eligible for a high school diploma. Students who are English learners are required to take the CAHSEE in grade ten with all students. However, the law says that during their first 24 months in a California school, they are to receive six months of special instruction in reading, writing, and comprehension in English. Additionally, English learners must be permitted to take the CAHSEE with certain test variations if used regularly in the classroom. A student who does not pass the exam in grade ten will have additional opportunities to pass it.

Preguntas Hechas Frecuentemente

A continuación encontrará respuestas a las preguntas más frecuentes sobre el Examen *California High School Exit Examination* o CAHSEE. Si tiene preguntas cuyas respuestas no aparezcan aquí, por favor llame al director de su escuela o a la oficina de evaluación de su distrito escolar. Puede encontrar respuestas a otras preguntas frecuentes en la página de Web del Departamento de Educación de California o *CDE* y del CAHSEE http://www.cde.ca.gov/ta/tg/hs/.

¿Qué cubre el CAHSEE?

El CAHSEE tiene dos secciones: inglés y matemáticas.

La sección de inglés del CAHSEE cubre los estándares estatales del contenido abarcando hasta el décimo grado inclusive. La parte correspondiente a la lectura incluye vocabulario, decodificación, comprensión y análisis de textos de información y textos de literatura. En la parte de escritura, el examen cubre estrategias de la escritura, aplicaciones y las reglas del inglés (por ejemplo gramática, ortografía y puntuación).

La parte de matemáticas del CAHSEE cubre los estándares estatales del sexto y séptimo grado y álgebra I. El examen incluye estadística, análisis de datos y probabilidad, teoría de los números, medidas y geometría, razonamiento matemático y álgebra. Se espera que los alumnos demuestren tener destreza en cómputo y aritmética, incluyendo la habilidad de trabajar con decimales, fracciones y porcentajes.

¿Qué clase de preguntas contiene el CAHSEE?

La mayor parte de las preguntas en el CAHSEE son preguntas de selección múltiple. Sin embargo, la sección de inglés también incluye una pregunta en forma de ensayo (*writing task*). El examen se administra en inglés solamente y todos los alumnos deben aprobarlo en inglés para recibir su diploma de preparatoria o *high school*. En esta guía de estudio y en la página de web del Departamento de Educación de California o *CDE*, hay ejemplos de preguntas que han aparecido en exámenes previos.

¿Cuándo toman los alumnos el CAHSEE por primera vez?

Los alumnos deberán tomar el examen por primera vez en la segunda parte de su décimo grado.

¿Cuándo (y cómo) sabrán los alumnos si aprobaron o no el CAHSEE?

Los distritos escolares reciben los reportes de las calificaciones obtenidas por sus alumnos aproximadamente siete semanas después de haber administrado el examen. Una copia se envía directamente a la casa del alumno y otra copia se archiva con el expediente permanente del alumno. Es importante que los padres o guardianes guarden una copia del reporte del alumno para sus archivos. El estado de California *no* retiene ninguna copia de los resultados. Los resultados de cada alumno son confidenciales.

Se publican solamente resultados de grupos (de escuelas enteras y distritos). Las calificaciones varían entre los 275 a los 450 puntos. Se requiere una calificación de 350 o más para aprobar.

¿Qué pasa si un alumno no aprueba la primera vez?

Los alumnos que no aprueben el examen en el décimo grado tendrán varias oportunidades de tomarlo de nuevo durante el 11º y el 12º grado. Una vez que hayan aprobado una de las dos secciones del examen no tendrán que tomar esa parte de nuevo. La ley estatal exige que los alumnos que no aprueben alguna parte del examen reciban educación adicional que les ayude a aprender lo que necesitan saber para aprobarlo. Cada escuela y cada distrito decidirá cómo proveer esa educación adicional. Para saber que tipo de ayuda hay disponible en la escuela de su hijo o hija y cuando el examen será administrado de nuevo, llame al director o al consejero de la escuela.

¿Qué pasa si un alumno ya tiene el 12mo grado y todavía no ha aprobado una o ambas partes del CAHSEE?

La ley (AB 347) estatal establece que los alumnos quienes no han aprobado una ubno ambas partes del CAHSEE para el final del duodécimo grado tienen el derecho de recibir servicios e instrucción intensiva hasta dos años académicos consecutivos después de culminar el duodécimo grado o hasta aprobar ambas partes del CAHSEE, dependiendo de lo que ocurra primero. También, la ley estatal establece que usted tiene el derecho de remitir una queja si no tuvo la oportunidad de recibir estos servicios, o si los servicios ya mencionados no fueron adecuados. Si desea remitir una queja formal por favor de comunicarse con el administrador escolar.

¿Qué pasa si un alumno tiene necesidades especiales?

Si un alumno tiene un Programa de Estudios Individualizado o *individualized education program*—también conocido como IEP por sus siglas en inglés o un Plan de Sección 504, estos deberán describir los arreglos especiales a los que el alumno tiene derecho al tomar el examen.

Las dos clases de arreglos especiales para tomar el CAHSEE son "adaptaciones" y "modificaciones". Es importante entender la diferencia entre estas dos clases de arreglos porque pueden afectar la calificación que el alumno obtenga en el examen.

Una **adaptación** no altera lo que el examen evalúa—por ejemplo, tomar descansos adicionales durante el examen o usar un cuadernillo de examen con letras grandes.

Una **modificación** cambia fundamentalmente lo que el examen está evaluando—por ejemplo, usar una calculadora en la parte de matemáticas o escuchar una grabación de las preguntas en la sección de inglés.

Los alumnos tienen derecho a cualquier adaptación o modificación para tomar el CAHSEE que haya sido estipulada en su programa de IEP o plan de Sección 504. Los alumnos que tomen el examen usando una *adaptación* recibirán una calificación como todos los demás. Sin embargo, los alumnos que usen una *modificación* recibirán su calificación numérica seguida de la palabra "MODIFIED" (MODIFICADA). Sin embargo, si el alumno obtiene 350 puntos o más, el director de la escuela del alumno debe pedir a petición de los padres o guardianes una exención o *waiver* a la junta escolar de su localidad. Este proceso lleva a cabo, en parte, con una presentación para la junta escolar de su localidad, demostrando pruebas que el alumno ha adquirido los conocimientos y las destrezas necesarias que de otra manera sean necesarias para aprobar el CAHSEE.

Puede encontrar más información acerca del proceso para pedir esta exención o waiver incluyendo una lista de posibles adaptaciones y modificaciones en la página de Web del Departamento de Educación de California o hablando con el director de su escuela.

¿Qué pasa si un alumno todavía está aprendiendo a hablar y leer inglés?
Todos los alumnos deben pasar el CAHSEE para obtener su diploma de preporatoria o *high school*.

Los alumnos que están aprendiendo inglés o *English learners* tienen que tomar el CAHSEE en el décimo grado como todos los demás. Sin embargo, la ley exige que durante sus primeros 24 meses en una escuela de California deberán recibir seis meses de educación especializada en lectura, escritura y comprensión del inglés. Ademas, estudiantes de inglés como segunda lengua tienen que ser permitidos de tomar el CAHSEE con ciertas variaciones del examen si se usan regularmente en el salón de clase. Todo alumno que no apruebe el examen tendrá otras oportunidades para hacerlo.

Information for Students

This Study Guide has been written just for you. To receive a high school diploma, you must pass the CAHSEE, and we want to make sure you do.

The Mathematics part of the CAHSEE consists of 92 multiple-choice questions. This Study Guide includes tips for answering the multiple-choice questions. Remembering these tips can help you pass the CAHSEE.

Tips for Preparing for the CAHSEE

❑ **Apply Yourself in the Classroom.**
The CAHSEE measures what you are learning and have already been taught in the classroom. More than any other preparation, attending your classes, paying attention in class, and doing your homework will help you pass the CAHSEE.

❑ **Get Help!**
If you have trouble understanding any part of your class work or this Study Guide, get help! Talk to a teacher, a counselor, your parents, your guardian, or students who have already passed the CAHSEE. Many students receive valuable help in study groups with other students.

Your school district offers special help for students who have not passed the exam. To find out what your school offers, ask your Math teacher or principal.

❑ **Use This Study Guide.**
Don't wait until the last minute. Find a place where it's easy to concentrate, and set aside some time each week to prepare. Starting early will ensure you have time to get help if you need it.

Tips for Using the Answer Document

❑ Use only a #2 pencil. Harder lead will be difficult to erase if you need to. Softer lead can leave smudges, and to the machine that scores the exam, a smudge can look the same as an answer you chose.

❑ Mark only one answer to each question. If you change an answer, erase the original answer completely.

❑ Be certain you are marking the right question on your answer document, especially if you skip a question you want to answer later.

Tips for Answering Multiple-Choice Questions

❑ **Relax!**
You don't have to answer every question correctly to pass the CAHSEE. If you become stressed, take a deep breath, relax, and focus on doing the best you can. You will have chances to retake the exam if you need to.

❑ **Take as Much Time as You Need.**
If you need extra time, you can keep working through the school day. Just tell the person administering the exam that you need more time.

❑ **Answer Easy Questions First.**
If a question gives you trouble, skip it and focus on the ones that you understand. After you have answered the easy questions, return to the questions you skipped.

❑ **Using an Answer Document**
Be certain you are marking the right question on your answer document, especially if you skip a question you want to answer later.

❑ **Make Notes in the Test Booklet (But <u>Not</u> on the Answer Document).**
Writing a note to yourself can help you think through a question. Also, if you skip a question and return to it, a record of your thinking will often help you understand a test question in a new way. As you read, you can underline, mark up the passage, and take notes in the test booklet.

❑ **Eliminate Answers You Know Are Wrong.**
If you are not sure about the answer to a question, cross out any choices you *know* are wrong.

❑ **If You Must, Guess.**
On the CAHSEE, wrong answers do not count against you, so, it is to your advantage to answer *every* question. Even if you guess, you have a one-out-of-four chance of answering correctly. If you can eliminate two out of the four choices in any question, you have a 50-50 chance of answering correctly.

❑ **Review Your Work!**
When you finish the last question, go back over the exam to review your thinking and correct any mistakes. If you guessed at a question, change your answer only if you have a good reason; often, your first instinct will be your best. Also, check your answer document for stray marks and erase them as cleanly as you can.

Tips for Answering CAHSEE Mathematics Test Questions

❑ **Don't Give up Without Going Partway.**
Some students give up if they think they can't solve the whole problem. But if you do as much as you can, you might be able to eliminate some answers—maybe even all but one.

❑ **You Don't Have to Read All the Answers to Start Working on a Problem.**
If the answers are confusing, it may be best to start in on the problem and then look at the answers once you have an idea of what's going on. Go back and forth between working on the problem and looking at the answers until they begin to make sense.

❑ **Reason Backwards From the Answers.**
This is especially important in some algebra questions. If you can't solve an equation, you can plug in the possible answers and see which one works. Sometimes just trying one answer helps you see what's going on.

❑ **Think About the Basic Concept; Be Sure You're Thinking About the Right Thing.**
Many of the items on the test just check to see if you know what terms mean and how to perform basic tasks. Be careful, for example, that you don't compute the *radius* when you really need the *diameter*, or confuse *slope* with *intercept*.

Now let's look at a couple of examples. *Many test items are easier than they look at first glance.* And usually, the computation—the arithmetic —will be simpler than what you have been doing in math class.

In these examples, we'll use several of the tips we've mentioned—but watch especially how we eliminate choices that are wrong.

Example 1

Sample CAHSEE Question

Tina is filling a 45 gallon tub at a rate of 1.5 gallons of water per minute. At this rate, how long will it take to fill the tub?

A 30.0 minutes

B 43.5 minutes

C 46.5 minutes

D 67.5 minutes   M02688

Solution
To find the correct answer to this question, you're supposed to divide 45 by 1.5 to get 30. But imagine that you're nervous and you can't decide whether to add, subtract, multiply, or divide.

So think about the situation and use what you know. The tub holds 45 gallons. Tina is putting in 1.5 gallons every minute. How much water is there after one minute? 1.5 gallons. What about *ten* minutes? That would be 15 gallons (10 times 1.5). So after 20 minutes Tina has 30 gallons, and 30 minutes is 45 gallons.

Let's look at a different strategy for the same problem. If the water were coming in at 1.0 gallon per minute, it would take 45 minutes to fill. But the water is coming in *faster*, so it will take *less* time to fill the tub. Only options A and B are less than 45 minutes. (You just eliminated options C and D!) But option B (43.5 minutes) is only *slightly* less, while 1.5 gallons per minute is quite a bit more than 1.0. So the correct answer must be option **A**.

Example 2

Sample CAHSEE Question

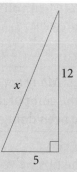

What is the value of *x* in the triangle shown above?

A   11

B   13

C   17

D   169

M02446

Solution

Here is a geometry question and a chance for making a *visual* estimate. You could use the Pythagorean theorem to solve the problem, but you don't have to. Look at the diagram. If it helps, you can make a "paper ruler" out of part of your booklet and use it to measure the diagram.

The length *x* has to be more than 12. But no way is it 169. So the answer is either 13 or 17. (You just eliminated options A and D!) But notice: 17 is the total distance along the two legs, 12 + 5. Segment *x* must be shorter than that, because it goes straight. So the correct answer is **B**.

Is it cheating to choose an answer without actually computing it? NO. It's demonstrating what you know and what you can do *on a multiple-choice exam*.

The test makers care that you know how big numbers are, that you understand variables, and that you can reason about geometric figures. They care that you know the basics well. But it's not so important whether you can do complicated arithmetic with paper and pencil.

Should you know how to compute the answer? Of course you should, and there will be many questions where you will have to compute or do some algebra to tell which answer is correct. But if you get stumped, some of these strategies might help you get a question correct.

Mathematics Practice Test

This is a practice test using sample CAHSEE questions to help you prepare for the CAHSEE. Answer all the questions in the practice test and then check your answers using the ANSWER KEY provided in the back.

When you take the actual CAHSEE, it will be separated into two sessions. Each session will contain 46 multiple-choice questions. Remember that you may take as much time as you need within the regular school day, and you will have a break between Sessions 1 and 2.

This practice test is designed to familiarize you with the CAHSEE test format and the possible types of items you might see on the real test. Since this practice test contains only a few samples of each standard, it cannot be used to accurately predict how you will perform on the CAHSEE.

Becoming familiar with the test may be helpful, but the absolute best way to do well on the mathematics portion of the test is to pay close attention in your math class, ask questions of others when you don't understand something, and complete all your homework. Learning mathematics, like learning another language, requires practice and repetition.

California High School Exit Examination

PRACTICE TEST

1. **Which number has the greatest absolute value?**

   A -17

   B -13

   C 15

   D 19

   M12795

2. **Between which two integers is the value of $\sqrt{61}$?**

   A   6 and 7

   B   7 and 8

   C   8 and 9

   D   9 and 10

   M22059

3. **Use the addition problems below to answer the question.**

   $$\frac{1}{2}+\frac{1}{4}=\frac{3}{4}$$

   $$\frac{1}{2}+\frac{1}{4}+\frac{1}{8}=\frac{7}{8}$$

   $$\frac{1}{2}+\frac{1}{4}+\frac{1}{8}+\frac{1}{16}=\frac{15}{16}$$

   $$\frac{1}{2}+\frac{1}{4}+\frac{1}{8}+\frac{1}{16}+\frac{1}{32}=\frac{31}{32}$$

   Based on this pattern, what is the sum of
   $$\frac{1}{2}+\frac{1}{4}+\frac{1}{8}+\frac{1}{16}+\ldots+\frac{1}{1024}?$$

   A $\dfrac{1001}{1024}$

   B $\dfrac{1010}{1024}$

   C $\dfrac{1023}{1024}$

   D $\dfrac{1025}{1024}$

   M21115

California High School Exit Examination

PRACTICE TEST

4. Traditions Clothing Store is having a sale. Shirts that were regularly priced at $20 are on sale for $17. What is the percentage of decrease in the price of the shirts?

   A   3%

   B   15%

   C   18%

   D   85%

   M30820

5. Which number equals $(2)^{-4}$?

   A -8

   B $-\dfrac{1}{16}$

   C $\dfrac{1}{16}$

   D $\dfrac{1}{8}$

   M10015

6. What is $\dfrac{3}{4} - \dfrac{1}{6}$?

   A $\dfrac{1}{6}$

   B $\dfrac{1}{3}$

   C $\dfrac{7}{12}$

   D $\dfrac{11}{12}$

   M13552

7. A salesperson at a clothing store earns a 2% commission on all sales. How much commission does the salesperson earn on a $300 sale?

   A $6

   B $15

   C $60

   D $150

   M20470

8. Some students attend school 180 of the 365 days in a year. About what part of the year do they attend school?

   A   18%

   B   50%

   C   75%

   D   180%

   M00047

9. What is the value of $\dfrac{2^6 \cdot 2^4}{2^5}$?

   A   4

   B   10

   C   16

   D   32

   M25206

California High School Exit Examination

PRACTICE TEST

10. John uses $\frac{2}{3}$ of a cup of oats per serving to make oatmeal. How many cups of oats does he need to make 6 servings?

    A $2\frac{2}{3}$

    B 4

    C $5\frac{1}{3}$

    D 9

    M23015

11. Which expression represents 0.0000007 in scientific notation?

    A 7×10^{-9}

    B 7×10^{-7}

    C 7×10^{7}

    D 7×10^{9}

    M20956

12. The Venn diagram below shows the number of girls on the soccer and track teams at a high school.

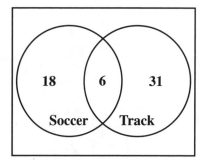

    How many girls are on both the soccer and track teams?

    A 6

    B 12

    C 49

    D 55

    M21162

California High School Exit Examination

13. These 8 cards are placed face down and shuffled.

If Beatrice turns over only one card, what is the probability she will get a card with a number less than 4?

A $\frac{1}{4}$

B $\frac{3}{8}$

C $\frac{1}{2}$

D $\frac{5}{8}$

M25304

14. The Smithburg town library wanted to see what types of books were borrowed most often.

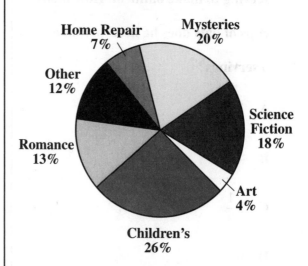

According to the circle graph shown above—

A more Children's books were borrowed than Romance and Science Fiction combined.

B more than half of the books borrowed were Children's, Mysteries, and Art combined.

C more Mysteries were borrowed than Art and Science Fiction combined.

D more than half of the books borrowed were Romance, Mysteries, and Science Fiction combined.

M02131

California High School Exit Examination

PRACTICE TEST

15. A restaurant is advertising 3-item combination specials that must include a main dish, a vegetable, and a drink.

Lunch Specials

Main Dish	Vegetable	Drink
Chicken	Broccoli	Water
Beef	Carrots	Soft drink
	Peas	Milk
	Corn	

How many 3-item combinations include a soft drink and corn?

A 2

B 3

C 4

D 8

M13738

16. Donald priced six personal Compact Disc (CD) players. The prices are shown below.

$21.00, $23.00, $21.00, $39.00, $25.00, $31.00

What is the median price?

A $21.00

B $24.00

C $27.00

D $30.00

M02964

California High School Exit Examination

PRACTICE TEST

17. Michelle read a book review and predicted that the number of girls who will like the book will be more than twice the number of boys who will like the book. Which table shows data that support her prediction?

A

	Number Who Liked the Book
Boys	35
Girls	40

C

	Number Who Liked the Book
Boys	70
Girls	25

B

	Number Who Liked the Book
Boys	35
Girls	80

D

	Number Who Liked the Book
Boys	40
Girls	40

M11882

California High School Exit Examination

PRACTICE TEST

18. Anna has the letter tiles below in a bag.

S T A T I S T I C S

She reached in the bag and pulled out an S. She then put the tile back in the bag. If Anna randomly selects a tile from the bag, what is the probability she will select an S again?

A $\dfrac{1}{5}$

B $\dfrac{2}{9}$

C $\dfrac{3}{10}$

D $\dfrac{1}{3}$

M25311

19. The scatterplot below shows the ages of some children and the distance each child lives from school.

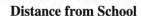

Distance from School

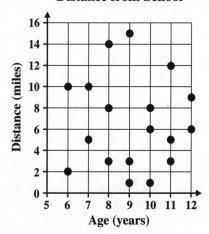

Which statement BEST describes the relationship between age and distance from school?

A As age increases, the distance from school increases.

B As age increases, the distance from school decreases.

C As age increases, the distance from school remains constant.

D There is no relationship between age and distance from school.

M10565

Practice Test

20. At a local bookstore, books that normally cost *b* dollars are on sale for 10 dollars off the normal price. How many dollars does it cost to buy 3 books on sale?

A $3b - 10$

B $3b + 10$

C $3(b - 10)$

D $3(b + 10)$

M10375

21. If a line passes through the points *A* and *B* shown below, approximately where does the line cross the *x*-axis?

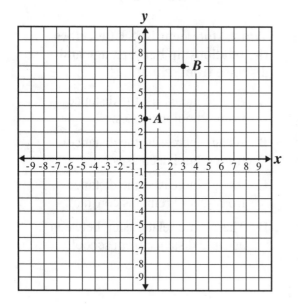

A   between -3 and -2

B   between 0 and -1

C   between 0 and 1

D   between 1 and 2

M10702

22. Which expression is equivalent to $7a^2b \cdot 7bc^2$?

A $14a^2b^2c^2$

B $49a^2bc^2$

C $49a^2b^2c^2$

D $343a^2b^2c^2$

M12872

PRACTICE TEST

23. **Mario drives 1500 miles every month. Which line plot correctly represents Mario's total miles driven over a period of six months?**

A

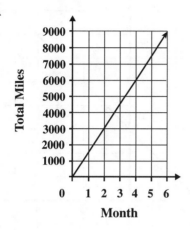

C

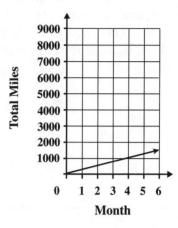

B

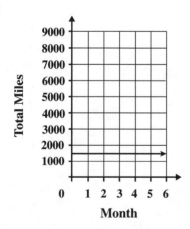

D

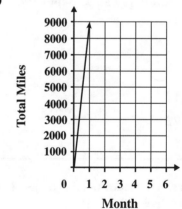

M11652

Practice Test

PRACTICE TEST

24. The temperature on a mountain peak was 7 degrees Fahrenheit (°F) at 6:00 p.m. By 8:00 p.m., the temperature had dropped to 0°F. If the temperature continued to drop at about the same rate, which is the BEST estimate of the temperature at 11:00 p.m.?

A $-20°F$

B $-14°F$

C $-10°F$

D $-9°F$

M20451

25. Brad bought a $6 binder and several packs of paper that cost $0.60 each. If his total was $13.20, how many packs of paper did Brad buy?

A   2

B   6

C   12

D   22

M12223

26. What is the value of $\left(3+5^2\right) \div 4 - (x+1)$ when $x = 7$?

A -7

B -1

C   8

D   10

M12963

27. What is the equation of the graph shown below?

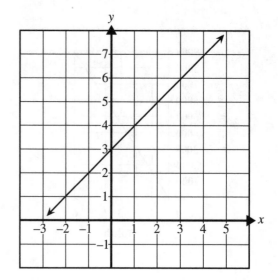

A $y = x - 1$

B $y = x + 1$

C $y = x + 3$

D $y = x - 3$

M02035

California High School Exit Examination

PRACTICE TEST

28. Which equation BEST represents the part of the graph shown below?

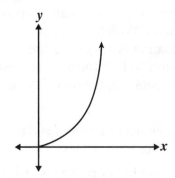

A $y = 1.75x$

B $y = 1.75x^2$

C $y = -1.75x$

D $y = -1.75x^2$

M10760

29. Lisa typed a 1000-word essay at an average rate of 20 words per minute. If she started typing at 6:20 p.m. and did not take any breaks, at what time did Lisa finish typing the essay?

A 6:40 p.m.

B 6:50 p.m.

C 7:00 p.m.

D 7:10 p.m.

M13652

30. What does x^5 equal when $x = -2$?

A -32

B -10

C $-\dfrac{1}{32}$

D 32

M12857

31. The graph below compares the weight of an object on Earth to its weight on the Moon.

An Object's Weight on the Moon

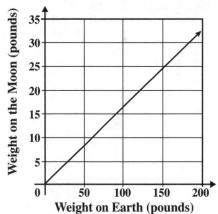

What is the approximate weight on the Moon of an astronaut who weighs 120 pounds on Earth?

A 15 pounds

B 20 pounds

C 25 pounds

D 30 pounds

M10668

Practice Test

32. A scale drawing of a horse is shown below.

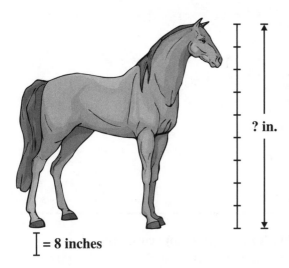

? in.

$\mathbb{I}$ = 8 inches

What is the actual height of the horse, in inches (in.), from the hoof to the top of the head?

A 56

B 64

C 72

D 80

M32040

33. A shipping company has 25 offices that shipped 60,000 packages last week. The offices were open 6 days and used 80,000 kilowatt-hours of electricity. Which pieces of information given above are necessary to find the average number of packages shipped per day last week?

A the number of offices and the number of packages

B the number of packages and the amount of electricity used

C the number of packages and the number of days open during the week

D the number of days open during the week and the amount of electricity used

M10538

34. A landscaper estimates that landscaping a new park will take 1 person 48 hours. If 4 people work on the job and they each work 6-hour days, how many days are needed to complete the job?

A 2

B 4

C 6

D 8

M11541

California High School Exit Examination

PRACTICE TEST

35. In the figure below, every angle is a right angle.

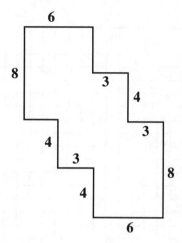

What is the area, in square units, of the figure?

A   96

B   108

C   120

D   144

M10790

36. A rectangular field is 363 feet long and 240 feet wide. How many acres is the field? $\left(1 \text{ acre} = 43{,}560 \text{ square feet}\right)$

A   2

B   3

C   4

D   5

M13918

37. The object below is made of ten rectangular prisms, each with dimensions of 5 centimeters (cm) by 3 cm by 2 cm. What is the volume, in cubic centimeters, of the object?

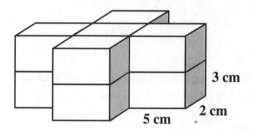

A   100

B   150

C   250

D   300

M30226

38. In the drawing below, the figure formed by the squares with sides that are labeled *x*, *y*, and *z* is a right triangle.

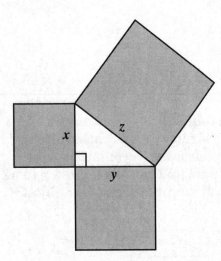

Which equation is true for all values of *x*, *y*, and *z*?

A $x + y = z$

B $x^2 + y^2 = z^2$

C $x^2 \cdot y^2 = z^2$

D $\dfrac{1}{2}xy = z$

M25150

39. A clothing company created the following diagram for a vest.

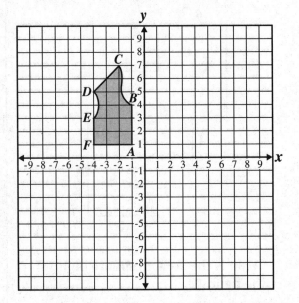

To show the other side of the vest, the company will reflect the drawing across the *y*-axis. What will be the coordinates of *C* after the reflection?

A $(2, 7)$

B $(7, 2)$

C $(-2, -7)$

D $(-2, 7)$

M10640

California High School Exit Examination

PRACTICE TEST

40. **What is the area, in square units, of trapezoid *QRST* shown below?**

$$\left[A = \frac{1}{2}h\left(b_1 + b_2\right) \right]$$

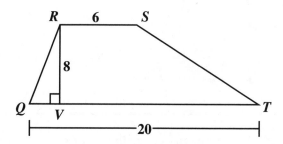

A   68

B   104

C   208

D   960

M12087

41. **One millimeter is—**

A $\frac{1}{1000}$ of a meter.

B $\frac{1}{100}$ of a meter.

C   100 meters.

D   1000 meters.

M00276

42. **In the diagram below, hexagon *LMNPQR* is congruent to hexagon *STUVWX*.**

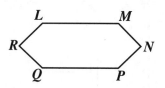

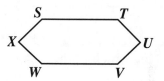

Which side is the same length as $\overline{MN}$?

A $\overline{NP}$

B $\overline{TU}$

C $\overline{UV}$

D $\overline{WX}$

M13069

PRACTICE TEST

43. Mia found the area of this shape by dividing it into rectangles as shown.

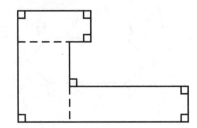

Mia could use the same method to find the area for which of these shapes?

A

C
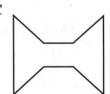

B

D
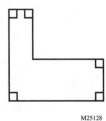

M25128

44. Simplify.

$$\left(x^2 - 3x + 1\right) - \left(x^2 + 2x + 7\right)$$

A $x - 6$

B $-x + 8$

C $-5x - 6$

D $2x^2 - x + 8$

M03355

45. What are the coordinates of the x-intercept of the line $3x + 4y = 12$?

A $(0, 3)$

B $(3, 0)$

C $(0, 4)$

D $(4, 0)$

M02462

46. Which of the following statements describes parallel lines?

A   Same y-intercept but different slopes

B   Same slope but different y-intercepts

C   Opposite slopes but same x-intercepts

D   Opposite x-intercepts but same y-intercept

M02610

California High School Exit Examination

PRACTICE TEST

47. Which graph represents the system of equations shown below?

$$y = -x + 3$$
$$y = x + 3$$

A

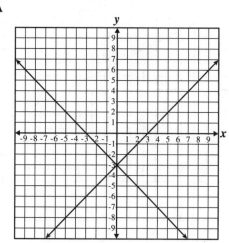

C

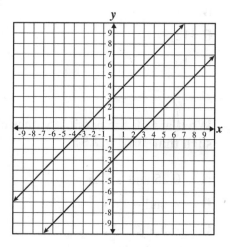

B

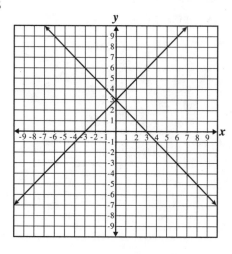

D

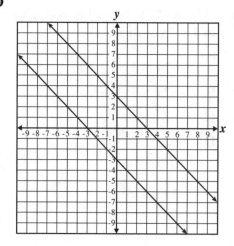

M12449

PRACTICE TEST

48. Yoshi has exactly one dollar in dimes (10 cents) and nickels (5 cents). If Yoshi has twice as many dimes as nickels, how many nickels does she have?

- **A** 4
- **B** 8
- **C** 12
- **D** 15

M02410

49. What are all the possible values of x such that $10|x| = 2.5$?

- **A** 0.25 and -0.25
- **B** 4 and -4
- **C** 4.5 and -4.5
- **D** 25 and -25

M12992

50. Which of the following is equivalent to $1 - 2x > 3(x - 2)$?

- **A** $1 - 2x > 3x - 2$
- **B** $1 - 2x > 3x - 5$
- **C** $1 - 2x > 3x - 6$
- **D** $1 - 2x > 3x - 7$

M02231

51. Which equation represents the line on the graph below?

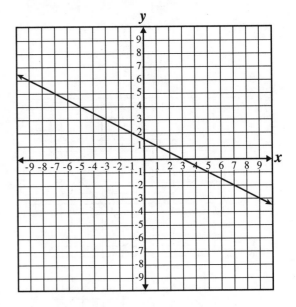

- **A** $x + 2y = 3$
- **B** $x + 2y = 5$
- **C** $2x + y = 9$
- **D** $4x + 2y = 3$

M22072

PRACTICE TEST

52. Colleen solved the equation $2(2x+5)=8$ using the following steps.

Given: $2(2x+5)=8$

Step 1: $4x+10=8$

Step 2: $4x=-2$

Step 3: $x=-\dfrac{1}{2}$

To get from Step 2 to Step 3, Colleen—

A divided both sides by 4.

B subtracted 4 from both sides.

C added 4 to both sides.

D multiplied both sides by 4.

M03139

53. What is the reciprocal of $\dfrac{ax^2}{y}$?

A $-\dfrac{ax^2}{y}$

B $-\dfrac{y}{ax^2}$

C $\dfrac{ax^2}{y}$

D $\dfrac{y}{ax^2}$

M13174

California High School Exit Examination

OVERVIEW OF THE STANDARDS

The mathematics part of the CAHSEE tests 6 broad categories, called strands. These strands come from grades 6 and 7, plus Algebra I. These are the formal descriptions of those 6 categories and the number of test questions from each category that appear on the CAHSEE.

❑ **Number Sense (NS):** Students demonstrate a foundational understanding of numbers and ways they are represented. (14 multiple-choice questions)
❑ **Statistics, Data Analysis, Probability (PS):** Students determine ways to collect, analyze, organize, and display data. (12 multiple-choice questions)
❑ **Algebra and Functions (AF):** Students formalize patterns, functions, and generalizations; work with algebraic symbols, expressions with variables, and graphical representations; understand different meanings and uses of variables; develop concepts of proportionality; and recognize and generate equivalent expressions, solve linear equations, and effectively use formulas. (17 multiple-choice questions)
❑ **Measurement and Geometry (MG):** Students select and use appropriate units; estimate and calculate measurements for the length, area, and volume of geometric figures; understand scaling in scale drawings and how changes in linear dimension affect area and volume; and solve problems involving dimensional analysis and conversion from one unit to another. (17 multiple-choice questions)
❑ **Mathematical Reasoning (MR):** Students analyze problems, use inductive and deductive reasoning, evaluate the reasonableness of solutions, generalize results, and apply them to new problems. (8 multiple-choice questions)
❑ **Algebra I (1A):** Students calculate with symbols and demonstrate symbolic reasoning. (12 multiple-choice questions)

These are the strands that will appear on your student score report. These broad categories are defined more specifically by "standards." The mathematics portion of the CAHSEE measures 53 standards. The pages following the Practice Test describe those standards, the types of test questions that measure the standards, and strategies you can use to pass the CAHSEE.

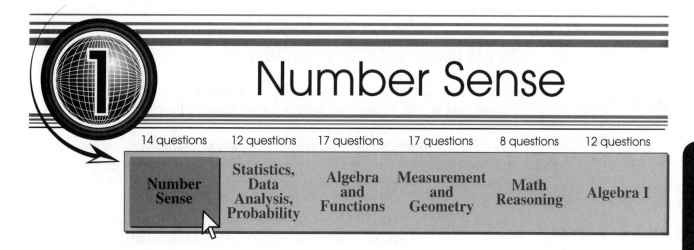

Number Sense

14 questions	12 questions	17 questions	17 questions	8 questions	12 questions
Number Sense	**Statistics, Data Analysis, Probability**	**Algebra and Functions**	**Measurement and Geometry**	**Math Reasoning**	**Algebra I**

Fourteen of the 80 CAHSEE math questions are based on 10 selected standards from the grade 7 Number Sense strand.

WHAT DO THE NUMBER SENSE STANDARDS ASK ME TO DO?

The CAHSEE Number Sense strand includes basic arithmetic calculations with whole numbers, fractions, and decimals, all done without using a calculator.

The CAHSEE Number Sense questions will ask you to:
- solve problems with fractions, decimals, percentages, and integers
- compare and order numbers
- understand percents, including percents less than 1% and greater than 100%
- use ratios and proportions to solve problems
- understand the meaning of numbers written in scientific notation
- find and use multiples, factors, and primes
- add, subtract, multiply, and divide numbers, and use the relationships among these operations including inverse, commutative, associative, and distributive properties
- estimate square roots of whole numbers to the nearest whole number

Vocabulary

The following words have appeared on the CAHSEE previously. If any of these words are unfamiliar to you, look them up in the CAHSEE Math Vocabulary list in the appendix at the back of this Study Guide, or check with your math teacher.

absolute value	integer	simple interest
compound interest	prime	square
decreased by	scientific notation	square root
equivalent expression		

WHY IS NUMBER SENSE IMPORTANT?

As an adult, you will use all the basic skills of arithmetic included in the Number Sense strand. You'll use your number sense skills as a consumer (nutrition choices, shopping for credit, choosing the best buy), as a U.S. citizen (taxes, voting issues), and as an employee (handling money, cost estimates, profit and loss, quality control). Many large companies give screening tests that include number sense knowledge for entry-level jobs.

The anchor problem for this strand, *Emergency Refrigerator!*, presents a situation that you may encounter when you rent your first apartment. But before we try *Emergency Refrigerator!*, let's first look at some sample CAHSEE questions, with solutions, that apply to this strand.

HOW WILL THE CAHSEE TEST MY KNOWLEDGE OF NUMBER SENSE?

The CAHSEE tests 10 of the 12 standards from the Number Sense strand for grade 7. Let's start by looking at 8 of these standards and some actual CAHSEE questions based on them. Each box that follows contains one of the standards, a sample question based on that standard, and a solution with explanation.

7NS1.1 Read, write, and compare rational numbers in scientific notation (positive and negative powers of 10) with approximate numbers using scientific notation. [1 question]

Sample CAHSEE Question

The radius of the earth's orbit is 150,000,000,000 meters. What is this number in scientific notation?

A 1.5×10^{-11}

B 1.5×10^{11}

C 15×10^{10}

D 150×10^{9}

M00213

Mathematical Solution	*Descriptive Solution*
• The correct answer is **B**. Please refer to the next column for a description of the solution.	Scientific notation is a short way to write very large or very small numbers using powers of 10. Here are some examples of the same numbers written first in the usual way and then in scientific notation: $$2000 = 2 \times 10^{3} \qquad 143,000 = 1.43 \times 10^{5} \qquad 0.0000234 = 2.34 \times 10^{-5}$$ A number in scientific notation is always written as a number greater than or equal to 1 but less than 10, times a power of 10. Looking at the possible answers for this CAHSEE question, you can see that options C and D are both incorrect because 15 and 150 are larger than 10. Also, in option A, the 10 has a negative exponent, so it would be a very small number. The correct answer must be B. But why? You can rewrite 150,000,000,000 as $15 \times 10,000,000,000$, which is 15×10^{10}. But 15×10^{10} is not yet in scientific notation because 15 is not a number between 1 and 10. So think of 15 as 1.5×10^{1}. Then $15 \times 10^{10} = (1.5 \times 10^{1}) \times 10^{10} = 1.5 \times 10^{11}$, choice **B**.

Number Sense

7NS1.2 Add, subtract, multiply, and divide rational numbers (integers, fractions, and terminating decimals) and take positive rational numbers to whole-number powers. [3 questions]

Sample CAHSEE Question

$$\frac{11}{12} - \left(\frac{1}{3} + \frac{1}{4}\right) =$$

A $\dfrac{1}{3}$

B $\dfrac{3}{4}$

C $\dfrac{5}{6}$

D $\dfrac{9}{5}$

M02048

Mathematical Solution

- $\dfrac{11}{12} - \left(\dfrac{1}{3} \cdot \dfrac{4}{4} + \dfrac{1}{4} \cdot \dfrac{3}{3}\right) =$

- $\dfrac{11}{12} - \left(\dfrac{4}{12} + \dfrac{3}{12}\right) = \dfrac{11}{12} - \left(\dfrac{4+3}{12}\right) =$

- $\dfrac{11}{12} - \left(\dfrac{7}{12}\right) = \dfrac{11-7}{12} = \dfrac{4}{12}$

- Reduce the fraction.
  $\dfrac{4 \div 4}{12 \div 4} = \dfrac{1}{3}$

- Therefore, the correct answer is **A**.

Descriptive Solution

One way to do this problem is to first find the least common denominator for the three fractions. Notice that the numbers 3, 4, and 12 all divide evenly into 12, so 12 is the least common denominator. Next, find equivalent fractions for $\dfrac{1}{3}$ and for $\dfrac{1}{4}$, each with 12 as the denominator:

$$\frac{1}{3} = \frac{1}{3} \cdot \frac{4}{4} = \frac{4}{12} \text{ and } \frac{1}{4} = \frac{1}{4} \cdot \frac{3}{3} = \frac{3}{12}$$

Finally, the numerators of these fractions can be combined to get the solution. You could write your work out like this:

$$\frac{11}{12} - \left(\frac{1}{3} + \frac{1}{4}\right) = \frac{11}{12} - \left(\frac{4}{12} + \frac{3}{12}\right) = \frac{11}{12} - \frac{7}{12} = \frac{4}{12}$$

But $\dfrac{4}{12}$ isn't an answer choice! You need to reduce $\dfrac{4}{12}$ to get $\dfrac{1}{3}$, so the correct answer is **A**.

7NS1.6 Calculate the percentage of increases and decreases of a quantity. [1 question]

Sample CAHSEE Question

The price of a calculator has decreased from $12.00 to $9.00. What is the percentage of decrease?

A   3%

B   25%

C   33%

D   75%

M02868

Mathematical Solution	*Descriptive Solution*
• $\dfrac{12-9}{12} \cdot 100 =$ • $\dfrac{3}{12} \cdot 100 =$ • $\dfrac{1}{4} \cdot 100 =$ • 25 • Therefore, the correct answer is **B**.	A price change from $12 down to $9 is a net decrease of $3. To find the percentage of decrease (or percentage of increase), the base is always the original or starting number, in this case $12. So, the correct percentage of decrease is $3 \div 12 = 25\%$, choice **B**. Notice that $3 \div 9 = 33\%$, option C, is not correct because $9 is the ending price, not the starting price.

7NS2.1 Understand negative whole-number exponents. Multiply and divide expressions involving exponents with a common base. [1 question]

Sample CAHSEE Question

$$\frac{10^{-2}}{10^{-4}} =$$

A 10^{-6}

B 10^{-2}

C 10^{2}

D 10^{8}

M02832

Mathematical Solution

- $\dfrac{10^{-2}}{10^{-4}} = \dfrac{10^{4}}{10^{2}}$

- $\dfrac{10^{4}}{10^{2}} = 10^{(4-2)} = 10^{2}$

      Or

- $\dfrac{10^{-2}}{10^{-4}} = 10^{-2-(-4)}$

- $10^{-2-(-4)} = 10^{2}$

- Therefore, the correct answer is **C**.

Descriptive Solution

When calculating with numbers written in scientific notation, it's important to know how to multiply and divide powers of ten.

Here are a few powers of 10 and their equivalents written in the usual way:

$$10^{4} = 10{,}000$$

$$10^{3} = 1000$$

$$10^{2} = 100$$

$$10^{1} = 10$$

$$10^{0} = 1$$

$$10^{-1} = 0.1 = \frac{1}{10}$$

$$10^{-2} = 0.01 = \frac{1}{100}$$

$$10^{-3} = 0.001 = \frac{1}{1000}$$

To simplify $\dfrac{10^{-2}}{10^{-4}}$, one way is to rewrite

$$\frac{10^{-2}}{10^{-4}} = \frac{\frac{1}{100}}{\frac{1}{10{,}000}} = \frac{1}{100} \div \frac{1}{10{,}000} = \frac{1}{100} \times \frac{10{,}000}{1} = 100 = 10^{2}$$

Therefore, the correct answer is 10^{2}, choice **C**.

Number Sense

7NS2.1 Sample CAHSEE Question cont'd

Another way is to remember that a negative power of ten is just the reciprocal of the positive power of ten. Using this idea, $10^{-2} = \dfrac{1}{10^2}$ and $\dfrac{1}{10^{-4}} = 10^4$, therefore:

$$\frac{10^{-2}}{10^{-4}} = \frac{10^4}{10^2} = 10^2.$$

A third way is to remember the "law of exponents" for dividing powers of the same base:

$\dfrac{a^m}{a^n} = a^{(m-n)}$. So for this problem,

$$\frac{10^{-2}}{10^{-4}} = 10^{(-2-(-4))} = 10^{(-2+4)} = 10^2.$$

7NS2.2 Add and subtract fractions by using factoring to find common denominators.
[1 question]

Sample CAHSEE Question

Which of the following is the prime factored form of the lowest common denominator

of $\dfrac{7}{10} + \dfrac{8}{15}$?

A $5 \cdot 1$

B $2 \cdot 3 \cdot 5$

C $2 \cdot 5 \cdot 3 \cdot 5$

D $10 \cdot 15$

M02826

Mathematical Solution

- Looking at the prime factors of the denominators,
  $10 = 2 \cdot 5$ and $15 = 3 \cdot 5$.

- Combining the smallest set of prime factors to both, you get $2 \cdot 3 \cdot 5$.

- Therefore, the correct answer is **B**.

Descriptive Solution

The denominators of these two fractions are 10 and 15. In order to add or subtract these fractions you would need to find a common denominator (a number that both 10 and 15 divide into evenly). One way to do this is to list the multiples of the larger number, 15, until you get a multiple that the smaller number also divides into evenly. Multiples of 15 are 15, 30, 45, 60, and so on. The lowest number in this list that 10 also divides into evenly is 30. Therefore, 30 is the least common denominator. So, which of the multiple choice answers multiplies out to 30? Only choice **B**, which is the correct answer.

But notice that standard 7NS2.2 says that you are to "use factoring to find the common denominator." According to the California standards, the proper way to do this problem is to first find the prime factorization of each denominator: $10 = 2 \cdot 5$ and $15 = 3 \cdot 5$. Then the common denominator is the product of the smallest set of prime factors that are common to both prime factorings, in this case $2 \cdot 3 \cdot 5$.

Notice that option C is incorrect. Even though $2 \cdot 5 \cdot 3 \cdot 5 = 150$, which is a common denominator, it is not the *least* common denominator; the factor 5 doesn't need to be included twice.

7NS2.3 Multiply, divide, and simplify rational numbers by using exponent rules.
[1 question]

Sample CAHSEE Question

$$\left(3^8\right)^2 =$$

A 3^4

B 3^6

C 3^{10}

D 3^{16}

M02406

Mathematical Solution	*Descriptive Solution*
• $\left(3^8\right)^2 = 3^{8\cdot 2} = 3^{16}$ • Therefore, the correct answer is **D**.	Sometimes it's difficult to remember how to use exponents. But you can answer these questions correctly if you understand how to use them. The exponent tells you how many times the base number is multiplied by itself. So, $\left(3^8\right)^2 = \left(3^8\right)\left(3^8\right) = (3\cdot3\cdot3\cdot3\cdot3\cdot3\cdot3\cdot3)\cdot(3\cdot3\cdot3\cdot3\cdot3\cdot3\cdot3\cdot3)$ $= 3^{16}$. Choice **D** is correct.

7NS2.4 Use the inverse relationship between raising to a power and extracting the root of a perfect square integer; for an integer that is not square, determine without a calculator the two integers between which its square root lies and explain why.
[1 question]

Sample CAHSEE Question

The square root of 150 is between—

A 10 and 11.

B 11 and 12.

C 12 and 13.

D 13 and 14.

M02666

Mathematical Solution	*Descriptive Solution*
• The correct answer is **C**. Please refer to the next column for a description of the solution.	The square root of a number is a number that can be multiplied by itself to get the original number. Some numbers have square roots that are integers, for example, 49. The square root of 49 is 7, because $7\cdot7 = 49$. But most numbers, like 150, do not have square roots that are integers. So, instead of figuring out the square root of 150, let's look at the squares of the answer choices for this question: $10\cdot10 = 100$; $11\cdot11 = 121$; $12\cdot12 = 144$; $13\cdot13 = 169$; $14\cdot14 = 196$. Because 150 is between 144 and 169, the square root of 150 must be between 12 and 13. The correct answer is **C**.

7NS2.5 Understand the meaning of the absolute value of a number; interpret the absolute value as the distance of the number from zero on a number line; and determine the absolute value of real numbers. [1 question]

Sample CAHSEE Question

If $|x| = 3$, what is the value of x?

A -3 or 0

B -3 or 3

C 0 or 3

D -9 or 9

M02122

Mathematical Solution	*Descriptive Solution*
• The correct answer is **B**. Please refer to the next column for a description of the solution.	The absolute value of a number is its distance away from 0 on the number line. So if $|x| = 3$, then x must be 3 units away from 0.  The number line above shows there are two such numbers, 3 and -3, so the correct answer is **B**.

USING NUMBER SENSE STANDARDS IN A REAL-LIFE SITUATION

You might be asking yourself, "When will I ever need to use this stuff?" To help you get the "big picture," the remaining two Number Sense standards are illustrated by a real-life problem *Emergency Refrigerator!* that a person might encounter after high school. Even though the CAHSEE doesn't include problems like this one, you might find it easier to remember one large problem—an "anchor problem"—in which many of the skills are combined, rather than trying to recall each of the standards individually.

Try to do this problem before you look at its solution on the following pages.

Emergency Refrigerator!

You're just getting comfortable living in your first apartment. Then—emergency! The old refrigerator left to you by the previous tenants stops working. You need to get a new refrigerator immediately. You decide on the brand and model of refrigerator you want and you have the following three options for purchasing it:

Option #1
Wagmen's Department Store has the refrigerator for $240, but this week only it is marked as part of the "red sticker sale." The red sticker means it will be sold at "1/4 off" the list price. Delivery is $20.

Option #2
The same refrigerator is advertised at Big Box Discount Appliances for $210. But you are lucky; this weekend only they have a coupon in the paper for 15% off the total cost of any item with a regular price over $100. Delivery costs $30.

Option #3
A friend works for Mike's Furniture and can get the same refrigerator for you for 20% over the wholesale price of $180. Your friend can use the company truck to deliver it for free.

You'll need to figure out the cost of each option before deciding what to do. Try to work out the cost of each option before going on to the next page. Remember, no calculators are allowed!

Emergency Refrigerator! Solution and Standards

Are you ready to check your answers to the *Emergency Refrigerator!* anchor problem? In order to figure the cost of the options, you need to use two of the Number Sense standards that are tested on the CAHSEE. The standards that apply in this situation, along with the number of questions on the CAHSEE that are based on that standard, appear to the left in the small print.

To decide which option has the lowest price, you'll need to calculate the cost of each option.

7NS1.3 Convert fractions to decimals and percents and use these representations in estimations, computations, and applications. [2 questions]

7NS1.7 Solve problems that involve discounts, markups, commissions, and profit and compute simple and compound interest. [2 questions]

Option #1

One-fourth of $240 is $60, the amount to be taken off. The sale price would be $240 − $60 = $180. But to get the refrigerator, you'll have to get it delivered for $20. So the total cost for Option #1 would be **$200**.

Option #2

Because the refrigerator costs more than $100, you can use the 15% off coupon to discount the selling price by 15%. One method is to first find 15% of $210. One way to think of 15% is "15 cents per dollar." So, 15% of $210 is $0.15 \cdot \$210$, which is $31.50. Then subtract $31.50 from the advertised price of $210, giving a sale price of $178.50.

Another way to figure the sale price is to realize that if you get 15% off, that means you need to pay only 85% of the advertised price. 85% of $210 is $178.50.

Finally, you need to add the $30 delivery charge, giving a total cost of **$208.50**.

Option #3

In order to figure the cost of this option, you need to find your price by adding on a 20% markup to the wholesale price of $180. Markups can be done in two ways. One way is to find 20% of $180, which is $36, and then add the $36 to the $180 to get the selling price of $216. Another way is to realize that if 20% is to be added on, then the selling price is 120% of the wholesale price. Then 120% of $180 is **$216**. Either way you do it, that's the total cost for Option #3 because there is no delivery charge.

You know that Option #1 costs $200, Option #2 costs $208.50, and Option #3 costs $216. Now that you've done the math, which option would you choose?

You've seen the 10 Number Sense standards; now you are ready for some additional practice. Answer the sample questions in the next section and then check your answers using the answer key provided in the appendix at the back of this Study Guide.

(Note: The CAHSEE questions used as examples throughout this Study Guide are questions that were used on prior CAHSEEs. These items will not be used in future CAHSEEs.)

ADDITIONAL NUMBER SENSE SAMPLE QUESTIONS

1. $3.6 \times 10^2 =$

    A 3.600

    B 36

    C 360

    D 3,600

    M00036

2. The five members of a band are getting new outfits. Shirts cost $12 each, pants cost $29 each, and boots cost $49 a pair. What is the total cost of the new outfits for all of the members?

    A $90

    B $95

    C $450

    D $500

    M00331

3. If Freya makes 4 of her 5 free throws in a basketball game, what is her free throw shooting percentage?

    A 20%

    B 40%

    C 80%

    D 90%

    M00223

4. The cost of an afternoon movie ticket last year was $4.00. This year an afternoon movie ticket costs $5.00. What is the percent increase of the ticket from last year to this year?

    A 10%

    B 20%

    C 25%

    D 40%

    M02158

5. Sally puts $200.00 in a bank account. Each year the account earns 8% simple interest. How much interest will be earned in three years?

    A $16.00

    B $24.00

    C $48.00

    D $160.00

    M02119

6. $4^3 \cdot 4^2 =$

    A 4^5

    B 4^6

    C 16^5

    D 16^6

    M02661

7. The square of a whole number is between 1500 and 1600. The number must be between—

   A   30 and 35.

   B   35 and 40.

   C   40 and 45.

   D   45 and 50.

   M00313

8. A CD player regularly sells for $80. It is on sale for 20% off. What is the sale price of the CD player?

   A $16

   B $60

   C $64

   D $96

   M02425

9. What is the absolute value of −4?

   A   −4

   B $-\frac{1}{4}$

   C $\frac{1}{4}$

   D   4

   M02667

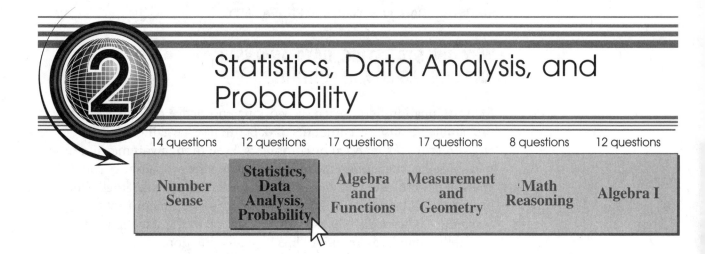

Statistics, Data Analysis, and Probability

14 questions	12 questions	17 questions	17 questions	8 questions	12 questions
Number Sense	Statistics, Data Analysis, Probability	Algebra and Functions	Measurement and Geometry	Math Reasoning	Algebra I

Twelve of the 80 CAHSEE multiple-choice questions are based on 7 selected standards from the Statistics, Data Analysis, and Probability strand for grades 6 and 7.

WHAT DO THE STATISTICS, DATA ANALYSIS, AND PROBABILITY STANDARDS ASK ME TO DO?

The CAHSEE questions from Statistics, Data Analysis, and Probability strand will ask you to:
- understand data displays including bar graphs and scatterplots
- find the mean, median, and mode of a data set
- express the probability of an event as a ratio, a decimal, or a percent
- know whether events are independent or dependent

Vocabulary

The words below have appeared previously on the CAHSEE. If any of these words are unfamiliar to you, look them up in the CAHSEE Math Vocabulary list in the appendix at the back of this Study Guide, or check with your math teacher.

bar graph	mean	probability
correlation	median	random
dependent events	pie chart	scatterplot
independent events		

WHY ARE STATISTICS, DATA ANALYSIS, AND PROBABILITY IMPORTANT?

Many occupations require a basic working knowledge of statistics and probability because vast amounts of data can now be gathered electronically and analyzed by computers. Even though you may not have to display the data, design the poll, or calculate the probabilities yourself, you will need to understand statistical information to make intelligent business decisions and healthy lifestyle choices. The anchor problem *Shipping Motorcycle Parts* illustrates how several of the statistics and probability standards are useful in a business situation.

But before we try *Shipping Motorcycle Parts*, let's first look at some sample CAHSEE questions, with answers, for this strand.

HOW WILL THE CAHSEE TEST MY KNOWLEDGE OF STATISTICS, USING STATISTICS, DATA ANALYSIS, AND PROBABILITY?

The CAHSEE tests 5 of the 14 grade 6 standards and all three of the grade 7 standards from the Statistics, Data Analysis, and Probability strand. Let's start by looking at 4 of these standards and some actual CAHSEE questions based on them. Each box that follows contains one of the standards, a sample question based on that standard, and a solution with an explanation.

6PS2.5 Identify claims based on statistical data and, in simple cases, evaluate the validity of the claims. [1 question]

Sample CAHSEE Question

The number of games won over four years for three teams is shown on the graph below.

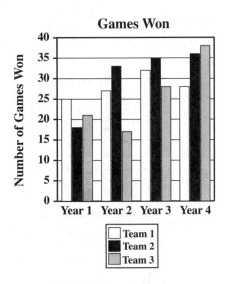

Games Won

Which statement is true based on this information?

A   Team 3 always came in second.

B   Team 1 had the best average overall.

C   Team 1 always won more games than Team 3.

D   Team 2 won more games each year than in the previous year.

M10300

Mathematical Solution

- The correct answer is **D**. Please refer to the next column for a description of the solution.

Descriptive Solution

To find the number of games a team won, find the top of the team's bar, then see which number the top of the bar is aligned with on the vertical line, or y-axis, labeled "Number of Games Won." For example, in Year 1, you can see that Team 1 won 25 games, because the top of the bar is aligned with the number 25 along the y-axis.

By reading the bar graph, you can see that Option A is not true because Team 3 came in second only in Year 1. To determine whether Option B is true, you must calculate the overall average, or mean, for each team. To find the mean for Team 1, you add the number of games won in each of the four years $(25 + 27 + 32 + 28 = 112)$; then divide by the number of years $(112 \div 4 = 28)$. Using this same method, you find that the overall average for Team 2 is 30.5 $(122 \div 4)$, and the overall average for Team 3 is 26 $(104 \div 4)$. Team 1 did not have the best overall average, so Option B is not true. Option C is not true because Team 3 won more games than Team 1 in Year 4. Option D is a true statement because Team 2 won more games each year than in the previous year. So the correct answer is **D**.

6PS3.1 Represent all possible outcomes for compound events in an organized way (e.g., tables, grids, tree diagrams) and express the theoretical probability of each outcome. [1 question]

Sample CAHSEE Question

To get home from work, Curtis must get on one of the three highways that leave the city. He then has a choice of four different roads that lead to his house. In the diagram below, each letter represents a highway, and each number represents a road.

Highway

Road	A	B	C
1	A 1	B 1	C 1
2	A 2	B 2	C 2
3	A 3	B 3	C 3
4	A 4	B 4	C 4

If Curtis randomly chooses a route to travel home, what is the probability that he will travel Highway B and Road 4?

A $\dfrac{1}{16}$

B $\dfrac{1}{12}$

C $\dfrac{1}{4}$

D $\dfrac{1}{3}$

M02512

Mathematical Solution	*Descriptive Solution*
• The correct answer is **B**. Please refer to the next column for a description of the solution.	The chart gives you an organized representation of the 12 possible routes that Curtis can follow. Because Curtis chooses his route randomly, each of the twelve possible routes shown in the chart is equally likely. Traveling Highway B and Road 4 is only one of these 12 equally likely possibilities. Therefore, the correct answer is **B**, $\dfrac{1}{12}$.

6PS3.3 Represent probabilities as ratios, proportions, decimals between 0 and 1, and percentages between 0 and 100 and verify that the probabilities computed are reasonable; know that if *P* is the probability of an event, 1-*P* is the probability of an event not occurring. [2 questions]

Sample CAHSEE Question

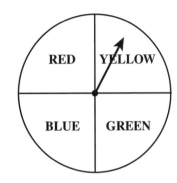

The spinner shown above is fair. What is the probability that the spinner will NOT stop on red if you spin it one time?

A $\dfrac{1}{4}$

B $\dfrac{1}{3}$

C $\dfrac{3}{4}$

D $\dfrac{4}{3}$

M00094

Mathematical Solution

- The correct answer is **C**. Please refer to the next column for a description of the solution.

Descriptive Solution

Because the spinner is "fair," this means that the four outcomes—"red," "yellow," "blue," and "green"—are each equally likely to be the result of a spin. Because three of the four possibilities are not "red," the probability of not spinning "red" is answer **C**.

Probability Statistics

**6PS3.5 Understand the difference between independent and dependent events.
[1 question]**

Sample CAHSEE Question

Heather flipped a coin five times, and each time it came up heads. If Heather flips the coin one more time, what is the theoretical probability that it will come up tails?

A $\frac{1}{6}$

B $\frac{1}{2}$

C $\frac{3}{5}$

D $\frac{5}{6}$

M02171

Mathematical Solution
- The correct answer is **B**. Please refer to the next column for a description of the solution.

Descriptive Solution
On any particular coin flip, the chance of getting a head or getting a tail is equally likely. Each flip that came before has no effect on the outcome of the next flip; each flip of the coin is *independent* of all the flips that came before. So, the probability of getting tails on the sixth flip is still $\frac{1}{2}$, choice **B**.

USING STATISTICS, DATA ANALYSIS, AND PROBABILITY STANDARDS IN A REAL-LIFE SITUATION

You might again be asking yourself, "When will I ever need to use this stuff?" To help you get the "big picture," the remaining three Statistics, Data Analysis, and Probability standards will be illustrated by a real-life problem that a person might encounter after high school: *Shipping Motorcycle Parts.* Even though the CAHSEE doesn't include problems like this one, you might find it easier to remember one large problem (an "anchor problem") where many of the skills are combined, rather than trying to recall how to do each of the standards individually.

Shipping Motorcycle Parts, Part 1

You work as a sales agent for Custom Motorcycle Parts Unlimited. When you make a sale, you tell your customers that their orders will be shipped "in about 10 working days." But lately you are getting a lot of calls back from your customers who haven't received their orders on time.

You call the production manager and ask how long it takes her employees to ship a typical order after they receive it. Because their computerized system collects data on how long it takes to make and send out each order, the production manager is able to supply you with a bar graph showing how many days it took to get orders out during the past six months:

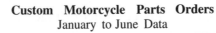

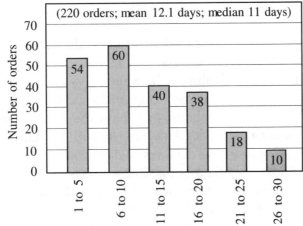

Custom Motorcycle Parts Orders
January to June Data

(220 orders; mean 12.1 days; median 11 days)

Number of orders / Number of days to produce and ship an order

- 1 to 5: 54
- 6 to 10: 60
- 11 to 15: 40
- 16 to 20: 38
- 21 to 25: 18
- 26 to 30: 10

The production manager also gives you the data for the ten orders shipped last week, the first week of July. The number of days to produce and ship each of the ten orders sent out last week were:

$$6, 15, 4, 19, 10, 21, 4, 17, 24, 20$$

Based on the data you have, what would you tell your customers about how many days it will take to produce and ship out their orders?

Before turning the page, find the mean and median of last week's data.

Compare your answers with the six-month data shown in the bar graph.

Shipping Motorcycle Parts, Part 1 Solution

The bar graph and last week's data give you the information you'll need so you can be more helpful to your customers.

First let's look at the data for last week:

$$6, 15, 4, 19, 10, 21, 4, 17, 24, 20$$

What was the average number of days for shipping an order last week? For this data, the average could be either the *mean* or the *median*.

To find the *mean* we need to find the sum of the data and then divide the sum by the number of data items.

$$6 + 15 + 4 + 19 + 10 + 21 + 4 + 17 + 24 + 20 = 140$$

Since there are ten data items we divide the sum by 10: $140/10 = 14$ days. So the mean number of days to produce an order for those shipped last week was 14 days.

To find the *median* of a data set, we start by putting all numbers in order. Last week's data, written in order from least to greatest is:

$$4, 4, 6, 10, 15, 17, 19, 20, 21, 24$$

For an odd number of data, the median is the middle number; for an even number of data, it's the average of the middle two numbers. In this case we have ten data items, an even number. The middle two numbers in the set are 15 and 17. So the median is the average of 15 and 17, which is 16 days.

Now look back at the bar graph that shows the data for the past six months. How does last week's data compare with the data in the bar graph? The mean of last week's data was 14 days, which is greater than the 12.1 day mean for the past six months. Last week's median of 16 days was also greater than the six month median of 11 days. The bar graph displays the distribution of the data. The bars on the graph show that almost half the orders are shipped out within 10 days, but 28 of the orders took 21 days or more.

So what should you tell your customers about shipping times? Based on this data, you might want to tell your customers to expect their order to be shipped in about 12 to 14 days, but some orders may take up to 30 days before shipping.

6PS1.1 Compute the range, mean, and median and mode of data sets. [3 questions]. (Note: The crossed out portion will not be tested on the CAHSEE.)

7PS1.1 Know various forms of display for data sets, including a stem-and-leaf plot or box-and-whisker plot; use the forms to display a single set of data or to compare two sets of data. [2 questions] (Note: The crossed out portion will not be tested on the CAHSEE.)

Shipping Motorcycle Parts, Part 2

You would like to give your customers more precise information about shipping times. From your experience you know that expensive orders take longer to produce and ship. So you get additional data about the price for each order shipped last week and make a scatterplot of the paired data.

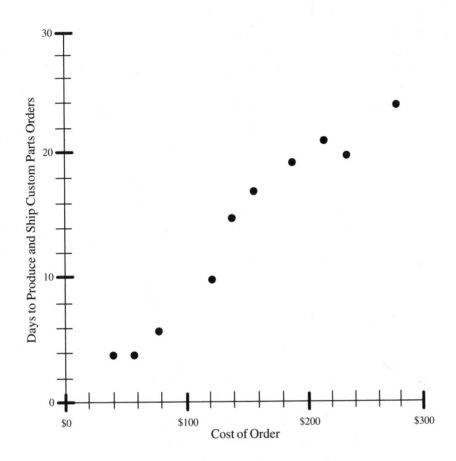

Does the scatterplot show a pattern? What does it tell you about the relationship between the cost of an order and the days it takes to send it out?

Based on the trend indicated by the scatterplot, about how many days will it take to produce and ship a $100 order? About how long for a $200 order?

7PS1.2 Represent two numerical variables on a scatterplot and informally describe how the data points are distributed and any apparent relationship that exists between the two variables (e.g., between time spent on homework and grade level). [2 questions]

Shipping Motorcycle Parts, Part 2 Solution

If you simply "eyeball" the trend in the scatterplot, it looks like a $100 order takes around seven or eight days to produce and ship; a $200 order takes about 18 to 20 days.

Now you are ready to test what you've learned by trying a few sample CAHSEE questions from the Statistics, Data Analysis, and Probability strand. Answer the questions in the next section and then check your answers using the answer key provided in the appendix at the back of this Study Guide.

(Note: The CAHSEE questions used as examples throughout this Study Guide are questions that were used on prior CAHSEEs. These items will not be used in future CAHSEEs.)

ADDITIONAL STATISTICS, DATA ANALYSIS, AND PROBABILITY SAMPLE QUESTIONS

1. **Three-fourths of the 36 members of a club attended a meeting. Ten of those attending the meeting were female. Which one of the following questions can be answered with the information given?**

   A How many males are in the club?

   B How many females are in the club?

   C How many male members of the club attended the meeting?

   D How many female members of the club did not attend the meeting?

   M00261

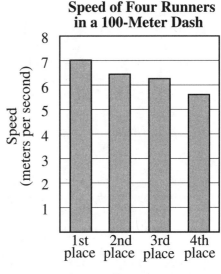

Speed of Four Runners in a 100-Meter Dash

2. **Mr. Gulati is holding five cards numbered 1 through 5. He has asked five students to each randomly pick a card to see who goes first in a game. Whoever picks the card numbered 5 goes first. Juanita picks first, gets the card numbered 4, and keeps the card. What is the probability that Yoko will get the card numbered 5 if she picks second?**

   A $\frac{1}{2}$

   B $\frac{1}{3}$

   C $\frac{1}{4}$

   D $\frac{1}{5}$

   M02145

3. **Based on the bar graph shown above, which of the following conclusions is true?**

   A Everyone ran faster than 6 meters per second.

   B The best possible rate for the 100-meter dash is 5 meters per second.

   C The first-place runner was four times as fast as the fourth-place runner.

   D The second-place and third-place runners were closest in time to one another.

   M00279

Probability
Statistics

4. **Which scatterplot shows a negative correlation?**

A
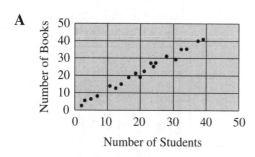

C
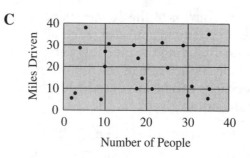

B
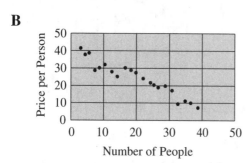

D
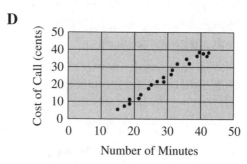

M02546

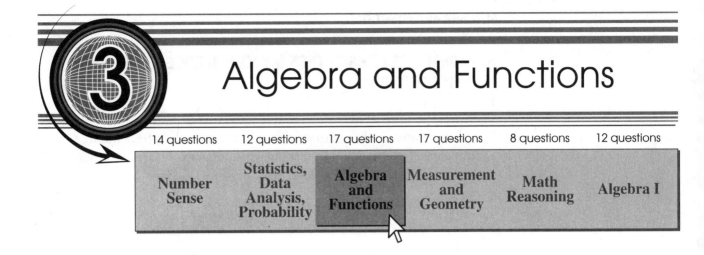

Algebra and Functions

14 questions   12 questions   17 questions   17 questions   8 questions   12 questions

| Number Sense | Statistics, Data Analysis, Probability | Algebra and Functions | Measurement and Geometry | Math Reasoning | Algebra I |

Seventeen of the 80 CAHSEE multiple-choice questions are based on 10 selected standards of the grade 7 Algebra and Functions strand.

WHAT DO THE ALGEBRA AND FUNCTIONS STANDARDS ASK ME TO DO?

To answer the CAHSEE Algebra and Functions questions, you'll need to know how to:

- generalize numerical and geometric patterns
- use a table, graph, or symbolic rule to represent the generalization of a pattern
- compare different forms of representations
- know the difference between a relation and a function
- solve linear equations

Vocabulary

The words below have appeared on the CAHSEE during past administrations. If any of these words are unfamiliar to you, look them up in the CAHSEE Math Vocabulary list in the appendix at the back of this Study Guide, or check with your math teacher.

expression   slope y-intercept
parallel x-intercept

WHY ARE ALGEBRA AND FUNCTIONS IMPORTANT?

Many entry-level technical, scientific, and health-related jobs require additional training beyond high school. To qualify for additional training for these higher-paying jobs, you need to know the basics of algebra. You can keep your career and college options open by mastering algebra basics while you are in high school.

The CAHSEE questions focus mainly on the basic algebra skills necessary to deal with graphs, formulas, linear functions, and equation solving. In fact, the Algebra and Function standards, together with the Algebra I standards, cover the exact same classic algebra topics that students in the United States have studied for more than one hundred years!

HOW WILL THE CAHSEE TEST MY KNOWLEDGE OF ALGEBRA AND FUNCTIONS?

The CAHSEE tests 10 of the 13 grade 7 standards from the Algebra and Functions strand. Each box that follows contains one of the standards, a sample question based on that standard, and an explanation of the question's solution.

7AF1.1 **Use variables and appropriate operations to write an expression, an equation, an inequality, or a system of equations or inequalities that represents a verbal description (e.g., three less than a number, half as large as area A). [2 questions]**

Sample CAHSEE Question

Which of the following inequalities represents the statement, "A number x, decreased by 13 is less than or equal to 39"?

A $13 - x \geq 39$

B $13 - x \leq 39$

C $x - 13 \leq 39$

D $x - 13 < 39$

M03049

Mathematical Solution

- A number x, decreased by 13 should be written as $x - 13$.

- Less than or equal to 39 should be written as ≤ 39.

- Combining these two parts, you get $x - 13 \leq 39$. Therefore, the correct answer is **C**.

Descriptive Solution

The first part of the sentence says "A number x, decreased by 13." Other ways of saying this that are commonly used in math textbooks include "13 less than a number x" or "the difference between a number x and 13" or "take away 13 from a number x." All of these phrases are written algebraically as "$x - 13$." The second part of the sentence, "is less than or equal to 39," would be written algebraically as "≤ 39." Therefore, the correct answer is **C**: $x - 13 \leq 39$.

Algebra Functions

7AF1.2 Use the correct order of operations to evaluate algebraic expressions such as $3(2x + 5)^2$. [1 question]

Sample CAHSEE Question

If $h = 3$ and $k = 4$, then $\dfrac{hk + 4}{2} - 2 =$

A   6

B   7

C   8

D 10

M00052

Mathematical Solution

- $\dfrac{3 \cdot 4 + 4}{2} - 2 = ?$

- $\dfrac{12 + 4}{2} - 2 = ?$

- $\dfrac{16}{2} - 2 = ?$

- $8 - 2 = 6$

- Therefore, the correct answer is **A**.

Descriptive Solution

The correct answer is **A**, 6. To simplify expressions, you need to use the proper algebraic order of operations: multiplication and division must be done before addition and subtraction. Substituting 3 for "h" and 4 for "k" in the expression gives the following as the solution.

$$\frac{3 \cdot 4 + 4}{2} - 2 = \frac{12 + 4}{2} - 2 = \frac{16}{2} - 2 = 8 - 2 = 6$$

7AF1.5 Represent quantitative relationships graphically and interpret the meaning of a specific part of a graph in the situation represented by the graph. [3 questions]

Sample CAHSEE Question

The cost of a long distance call charged by each of two telephone companies is shown on the graph below.

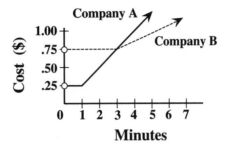

Company A is less expensive than Company B for—

A all calls.

B 3 minute calls only.

C calls less than 3 minutes.

D calls longer than 3 minutes.

M02840

Mathematical Solution	*Descriptive Solution*
• The correct answer is **C**. Please refer to the next column for a description of the solution.	The graph shows that, for all calls lasting less than three minutes, Company B charges a flat rate of 75¢. But for these calls, Company A's prices are all under 75¢. For calls longer than 3 minutes, Company B's prices are cheaper. So, the correct answer is **C**.

Algebra Functions

7AF2.1 Interpret positive whole-number powers as repeated multiplication and negative whole-number powers as repeated division or multiplication by the multiplicative inverse. Simplify and evaluate expressions that include exponents. [1 question]

Sample CAHSEE Question

$x^3 y^3 =$

A $9xy$

B $(xy)^6$

C $3xy$

D $xxxyyy$

M02879

Mathematical Solution

- $x^3 = xxx$

- $y^3 = yyy$

- Combining these parts, you get $xxxyyy$.

- Therefore, the correct answer is **D**.

Descriptive Solution

Raising a number to the third power means multiplying the number by itself three times. For example, $5^3 = (5)(5)(5) = 25(5) = 125$. For any number x, $x^3 = xxx$. Therefore, the correct answer is **D**, $xxxyyy$.

7AF2.2 Multiply and divide monomials; extend the process of taking powers and extracting roots to monomials when the latter results in a monomial with an integer exponent. [1 question]

Sample CAHSEE Question

Simplify the expression shown below.

$$\left(6a^4bc\right)\left(7ab^3c\right)$$

A $13a^4b^3c$

B $13a^5b^4c^2$

C $42a^4b^3c$

D $42a^5b^4c^2$

M02109

Mathematical Solution

$$=6(7)a^4abb^3cc$$

$$=42a^{4+1}b^{1+3}c^{1+1}$$

$$=42a^5b^4c^2$$

- Therefore, the correct answer is **D**.

                    Or

$$=(6aaaabc)(7abbbc)$$

$$=42aaaaabbbbcc$$

$$=42a^5b^4c^2$$

- Therefore, the correct answer is **D**.

Descriptive Solution

You may use the exponent rule that allows the addition of the powers when the bases are multiplied or the correct answer for this question may be even easier to see if we write out the expression using expanded notation like this:

$$\left(6a^4bc\right)\left(7ab^3c\right)=\left(6aaaabc\right)\left(7abbbc\right)=$$
$$42aaaaabbbbcc=42a^5b^4c^2,\text{ which is}$$
choice **D**.

**7AF3.1 Graph functions of the form $y = nx^2$ and $y = nx^3$ and use in solving problems.
[1 question]**

Sample CAHSEE Question

Which of the following could be the graph of $y = x^3$?

A

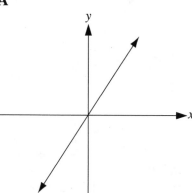

C

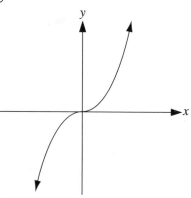

B

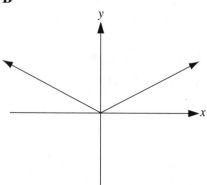

D

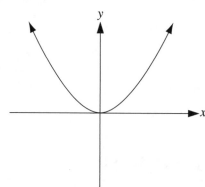

M02200

Mathematical Solution
- The correct answer is **C**. Please refer to the next column for a description of the solution.

Descriptive Solution
The correct answer is **C**. The other graphs shown may also be familiar to you.
Option A is the graph of a linear function, such as $y = nx$. Option B is the graph of an absolute value function such as $y = |nx|$.
Option D might be the graph of a parabola such as $y = nx^2$.

7AF3.3 Graph linear functions, noting that the vertical change (change in *y*-value) per unit of horizontal change (change in *x*-value) is always the same and know that the ratio ("rise over run") is called the slope of a graph. [2 questions]

Sample CAHSEE Question

What is the slope of the line shown in the graph below?

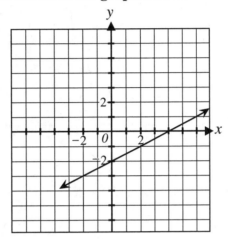

A -2

B $-\dfrac{1}{2}$

C $\dfrac{1}{2}$

D 2

M02556

Mathematical Solution

- Find the slope of the line by choosing two points. For example $(0,-2)$ and $(4,0)$.

- The slope $= \dfrac{\text{rise}}{\text{run}}$.

$$= \frac{\left(y\text{-coordinate of first point}\right)-\left(y\text{-coordinate of second point}\right)}{\left(x\text{-coordinate of first point}\right)-\left(x\text{-coordinate of second point}\right)}$$

$$= \frac{(-2)-(0)}{(0)-(4)}$$

$$= \frac{-2}{-4}$$

$$= \frac{1}{2}$$

- Therefore, the correct answer is **C**.

Descriptive Solution

The slope of the line shown in this graph can be found by first choosing any two points on the line. For this graph, the *y*-intercept, at $(0,-2)$, and the *x*-intercept, at $(4,0)$, will work nicely. If we move from the first point to the second, what is the net vertical change? The change in *y*-coordinates, from -2 to 0, is a <u>rise of 2 units</u>. And what is the horizontal change? Going from an *x*-coordinate of 0 over to 4 is a horizontal <u>run of 4 units</u>.

Algebra Functions

7AF3.3 Sample CAHSEE Question cont'd	
	The slope of the line is the ratio of the vertical rise to the horizontal run, which is $\frac{2}{4} = \frac{1}{2}$; therefore, the correct answer is **C**. Notice that this ratio always reduces to $\frac{1}{2}$ no matter which two points on the line are used.

7AF3.4 Plot the values of quantities whose ratios are always the same (e.g., cost to the number of an item, feet to inches, circumference to diameter of a circle). Fit a line to the plot and understand that the slope of a line equals the quantities. [1 question]

Sample CAHSEE Question

The graph below shows Francine's electric bill for 4 different months. What is the price per kilowatt-hour of Francine's electricity?

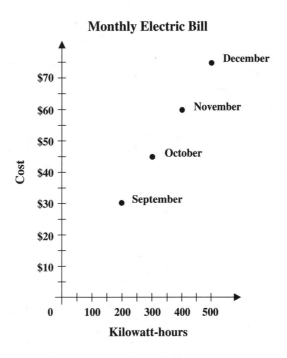

Monthly Electric Bill

A $0.15

B $0.30

C $1.50

D $6.67

M02681

Mathematical Solution

- Verify that the given points form a line.

- Find the slope of the line by choosing two points. For example $(200, 30)$ and $(300, 45)$.

- The slope $= \dfrac{\text{rise}}{\text{run}}$.

$$= \frac{(y\text{-coordinate of first point}) - (y\text{-coordinate of second point})}{(x\text{-coordinate of first point}) - (x\text{-coordinate of second point})}$$

$$= \frac{(45) - (30)}{(300) - (200)}$$

Descriptive Solution

The slope of a line equals the change in rise over the change in run. For example, from October to September, the change in rise (the vertical or y-axis marked "Cost") is 15 (45 – 30) and the change in run (the horizontal or x-axis marked "Kilowatt-hours") is

7AF3.4 Sample CAHSEE Question cont'd

$$= \frac{15}{100}$$

$= 0.15,$ which is equivalent to $0.15.

- Therefore, the correct answer is **A**.

                    Or

- Verify that the given points form a line.

- Choose one of the given points, for example $(200, 30)$.

- Since the question is asking for "price per kilowatt-hour," take $30 ÷ 200 kilowatt-hours.

  $= 0.15,$ which is equivalent to $0.15.

- Therefore, the correct answer is **A**.

100 (300 – 200). Therefore, the slope of the line is 0.15, or $\dfrac{15}{100}$. You will get this same number if you calculate the slope from November to October and from December to November. Because the data points for each month form a straight line, you know that the slope of the line is constant and that the price per kilowatt-hour is the same for each month. Therefore, you can use just one of the data points to calculate the answer.

The data point for September falls over the number 200 on the x-axis labeled "Kilowatt-hours," so you know that Francine used 200 kilowatt-hours during this month. To determine Francine's electric bill for September, you must trace the data point for September to the vertical line, or y-axis, which is marked "Cost." The data point is aligned with $30, so you can see that Francine spent $30 to use 200 kilowatt-hours in September. To determine the cost of each kilowatt-hour, divide the cost by the number of kilowatt-hours

$$\left(\frac{30}{200} = 0.15 \right).$$

Therefore, the correct answer is **A**.

7AF4.1 Solve two-step linear equations and inequalities in one variable over the rational numbers, interpret the solution or solutions in the context from which they arose, and verify the reasonableness of the results. [3 questions]

Sample CAHSEE Question

Solve for *x*.

$2x - 3 = 7$

A -5

B -2

C 2

D 5

M02771

Mathematical Solution

$$2x - 3 = 7$$
$$+3 \quad +3$$
$$2x = 10$$
$$\frac{2x}{2} = \frac{10}{2}$$
$$x = 5$$

• Therefore, the correct answer is **D**.

Descriptive Solution

Notice that this is a "two step" equation. You could solve the equation by first adding 3 to both sides, and then dividing both sides by 2. Another way is to check each of the answers to see which one makes the equation true. If you put 5 into the left-hand side of the equation, then $2(5) - 3 = 7$. So, the correct answer is **D**: 5.

Algebra Functions

7AF4.2 Solve multistep problems involving rate, average speed, distance, and time or a direct variation. [2 questions]

Sample CAHSEE Question

Stephanie is reading a 456-page book. During the past 7 days she has read 168 pages. If she continues reading at the same rate, how many more days will it take her to complete the book?

A   12

B   14

C   19

D   24

M00380

Mathematical Solution

- Find the rate:
  $168 \div 7 = 24$ pages per day.

- Find the number of pages she has left to complete the book:
  $456 - 168 = 288$ pages.

- Find the number of days left to complete the book:
  $288 \div 24 = 12$ days.

- Therefore, the correct answer is **A**.

Or

- Set up a proportion:
  $\dfrac{7}{168} = \dfrac{x}{456}$, where x represents the total number of days needed to read 456 pages.

  $168x = 7(456)$

  $168x = 3192$

  $\dfrac{168x}{168} = \dfrac{3192}{168}$

  $x = 19$ days

- Then subtract the number of days she has read the book so far, from the total number of days needed to read 456 pages: $19 - 7 = 12$.

- Therefore, the correct answer is **A**.

Descriptive Solution

You can do this problem without algebra. Notice that because Stephanie read 168 pages in seven days, she is averaging 24 pages per day. There are $456 - 168 = 288$ pages left to read. So at a rate of 24 pages a day, how long will it take Stephanie to read the remaining 288 pages? Well, 288 divided by $24 = 12$ days. So the correct answer is **A**. You could do this problem using algebra by setting up a proportion $\dfrac{7}{168} = \dfrac{x}{456}$. Solving for x you get 19 days total to read the book. But because Stephanie has already read for seven days, she'll have to read for 12 more days to finish.

Now that you've seen the 10 Algebra and Functions standards and read the solutions to some of the CAHSEE questions, it's time for you to answer the questions in the next section and then check your answers using the answer key provided in the appendix at the back of this Study Guide.

(Note: The CAHSEE questions used as examples throughout this Study Guide and in the following sample questions were used on prior CAHSEEs. These items will not be used in future CAHSEEs.)

ADDITIONAL ALGEBRA AND FUNCTIONS SAMPLE QUESTIONS

1. A shopkeeper has x kilograms of tea in stock. He sells 15 kilograms and then receives a new shipment weighing $2y$ kilograms. Which expression represents the weight of the tea he now has?

   A $x - 15 - 2y$

   B $x + 15 + 2y$

   C $x + 15 - 2y$

   D $x - 15 + 2y$

   M00110

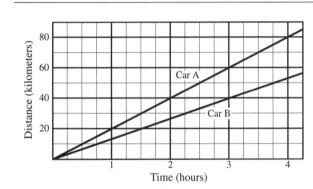

2. After three hours of travel, Car A is about how many kilometers ahead of Car B?

   A 2

   B 10

   C 20

   D 25

   M00066

3. Simplify the expression shown below.

   $$\left(5x^2z^2\right)\left(8xz^3\right)$$

   A $40x^2z^6$

   B $40x^3z^5$

   C $40x^3z^6$

   D $40x^5z^5$

   M02009

4. $\sqrt{4x^4} =$

   A 2

   B $2x$

   C $4x$

   D $2x^2$

   M03067

5. The slope of the line shown below is $\dfrac{2}{3}$.

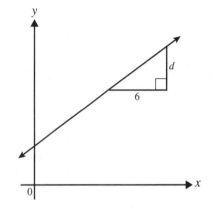

   What is the value of d?

   A 3

   B 4

   C 6

   D 9

   M02078

6. Solve for n.

   $$2n + 3 < 17$$

   A $n < 2$

   B $n < 3$

   C $n < 5$

   D $n < 7$

   M02040

7. In the inequality $2x + \$10{,}000 \geq \$70{,}000$, x represents the salary of an employee in a school district. Which phrase most accurately describes the employee's salary?

    A At least $30,000

    B At most $30,000

    C Less than $30,000

    D More than $30,000

    M02621

8. Robert's toy car travels at 40 centimeters per second (cm/sec) at high speed and 15 cm/sec at low speed. If the car travels for 15 seconds at high speed and then 30 seconds at low speed, what distance would the car have traveled?

    A 1050 cm

    B 1200 cm

    C 1425 cm

    D 2475 cm

    M10748

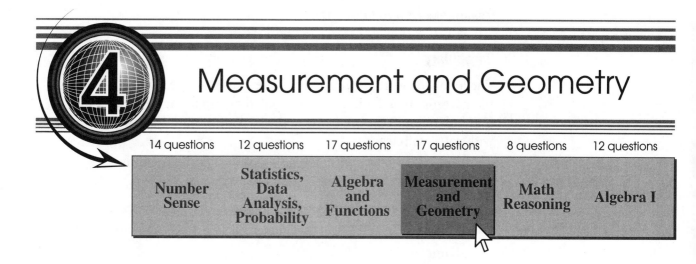

Measurement and Geometry

14 questions   12 questions   17 questions   17 questions   8 questions   12 questions

| Number Sense | Statistics, Data Analysis, Probability | Algebra and Functions | Measurement and Geometry | Math Reasoning | Algebra I |

Seventeen of the 80 CAHSEE math questions are based on 10 selected standards from the grade 7 Measurement and Geometry strand.

WHAT DO THE MEASUREMENT AND GEOMETRY STANDARDS ASK ME TO DO?

The CAHSEE Measurement and Geometry questions will ask you to:
- convert measurements and rates from one measuring system to another
- use information from scale drawings
- know the effect of scaling on length, perimeter, area, and volume
- translate and reflect a shape drawn on a coordinate system
- know the Pythagorean theorem and its converse, and how and when to use each
- know that congruent objects have the same shape and size
- use lengths of an object to calculate the object's area, surface area, or volume

Specifically, you need to know how to calculate each of the following items:
- perimeter of a polygon (add up the lengths of the sides)
- circumference of a circle ($C = \pi d$ where d is the diameter)
- area of a parallelogram ($A = bh$ where b is base and h is height; the formula $A = bh$ also applies for finding the area of a rectangle because rectangles are just special kinds of parallelograms.)
- area of a triangle $\left(A = \dfrac{1}{2}bh \right)$
- volume of a rectangular solid ($V = lwh$ where l is length, w is width, and h is height)

Note: The formulas above are not provided on the exam, but all other formulas will be provided for you.

Measurement Geometry

Vocabulary

The following words have appeared previously on the CAHSEE. If any of these words are unfamiliar to you, look them up in the CAHSEE Math Vocabulary list in the appendix at the back of this Study Guide, or check with your math teacher.

area	hypotenuse	radius
circle	parallel	surface area
circumference	parallelogram	trapezoid
congruent	perimeter	volume
diameter		

WHY ARE MEASUREMENT AND GEOMETRY IMPORTANT?

The mathematics from the Measurement and Geometry strand is used in architecture, landscaping, computer graphics, and the arts—and is also a foundation for calculus and other mathematics. The "anchor problem" for this strand, *Paving a Playground*, is from the building and construction trades and involves the use of many of the standards from this strand. But before we try *Paving a Playground*, let's first look at some sample CAHSEE questions, with answers, for this strand.

HOW WILL THE CAHSEE TEST MY KNOWLEDGE OF MEASUREMENT, USING MEASUREMENT, AND GEOMETRY?

The CAHSEE tests 10 of the 13 grade 7 standards from the Measurement and Geometry strand. Let's start by looking at 4 of these standards and the actual CAHSEE questions based on them. Each box that follows contains one of the standards, a sample question based on that standard, and a solution with explanation.

7MG2.2 Estimate and compute the area of more complex or irregular two- and three-dimensional figures by breaking the figures down into more basic geometric objects. [2 questions]

Sample CAHSEE Question

One-inch cubes are stacked as shown in the drawing below.

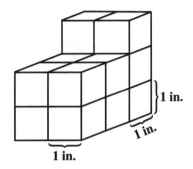

What is the <u>total</u> surface area?

A 19 in.^{2}

B 29 in.^{2}

C 32 in.^{2}

D 38 in.^{2}

M02812

Mathematical Solution

- Add all faces,
  $4+7+7+6+6+4+2+2=38$

- Therefore, the correct answer is **D**.

Descriptive Solution

Did you think the answer was 14? If so, you found the *volume* of this solid—it takes 14 cubes to build, so the volume is 14 cubic units. But this problem calls for surface area. What is surface area? If you put a solid object in water, the surface area of the object is the part that gets wet—the area of the outside surface. To find the total surface area of the solid above, you need to count up the number of square inches it takes to cover the outside, including the parts not visible in the picture. This object has several plane surfaces. Let's list the surfaces and the area of each: front, 4; right side, 7; left side (you don't see this one), 7; back, 6; bottom (you don't see this either), 6; top front, 4; top back, 2; and, finally, the front of the top two cubes, 2. Add these up and you get the total surface area: $4+7+7+6+6+4+2+2=38$ square inches. So the correct answer is **D**.

7MG2.3 Compute the length of the perimeter, the surface area of the faces, and the volume of a three-dimensional object built from rectangular solids. Understand that when the lengths of all dimensions are multiplied by a scale factor, the surface area is multiplied by the square of the scale factor and volume is multiplied by the cube of the scale factor. [1 question]

Sample CAHSEE Question

Bonni has two similar rectangular boxes. The dimensions of box 1 are twice those of box 2. How many times greater is the volume of box 1 than the volume of box 2?

A 3

B 6

C 8

D 9

M21061

Mathematical Solution

- $V_{Box\,1} = l \cdot w \cdot h$

- $V_{Box\,2} = 2l \cdot 2w \cdot 2h$
  $$= 2 \cdot 2 \cdot 2 \cdot l \cdot w \cdot h$$
  $$= 8 \cdot l \cdot w \cdot h$$

- Therefore, the correct answer is **C**.

Descriptive Solution

To answer this question, picture two rectangular boxes, one with dimensions that are twice those of the other:

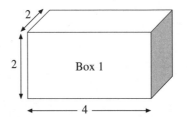 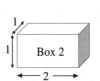

For this problem, imagine that box 2 has a length of 2, a width of 1, and a height of 1. The problem states that box 1 has dimensions twice those of box 2, so box 1 must have a length of 4, a width of 2, and height of 2.

The volume of each box can be found by multiplying its length by its width by its height $\left(V = lwh\right)$. Using this formula shows that the volume of box 1 is 16 $\left(V = 4 \cdot 2 \cdot 2\right)$ and the volume of box 2 is 2 $\left(V = 2 \cdot 1 \cdot 1\right)$. To determine how many times greater the volume of box 1 is, divide its volume by the volume of box 2, $\left(\dfrac{16}{2} = 8\right)$.

Therefore, the correct answer is **C**.

7MG3.2 Understand and use coordinate graphs to plot simple figures, determine lengths and areas related to them, and determine their image under translations and reflections. [2 questions]

Sample CAHSEE Question

The points $(1, 1), (2, 3), (4, 3),$ and $(5, 1)$ are the vertices of a polygon. What type of polygon is formed by these points?

A Triangle

B Trapezoid

C Parallelogram

D Pentagon

M02718

Mathematical Solution

- The correct answer is **B**. Please refer to the next column for a description of the solution.

Descriptive Solution

You'll want to plot these points on a grid to see what shape is formed. For each point, the first coordinate (*x*-coordinate) tells how far across to go, while the second coordinate (*y*-coordinate) tells how far up or down.

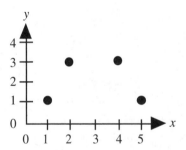

If you imagine these points connected in order with straight lines, you can see the correct answer must be **B**, trapezoid.

7MG3.3 **Know and understand the Pythagorean theorem and its converse and use it to find the length of the missing side of a right triangle and the lengths of other line segments and, in some situations, empirically verify the Pythagorean theorem by direct measurement. [2 questions]**

Sample CAHSEE Question

The club members hiked 3 kilometers north and 4 kilometers east, but then went directly home as shown by the dotted line. How far did they travel to get home?

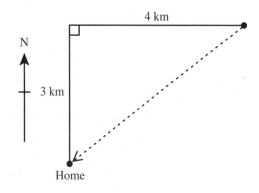

A   4 km

B   5 km

C   6 km

D   7 km   <small>M00120</small>

Mathematical Solution

- Use the Pythagorean theorem, $a^2 + b^2 = c^2$.

- $3^2 + 4^2 = c^2$

- $9 + 16 = c^2$

- $25 = c^2$

- $\sqrt{25} = c$

- $5 = c$

- Therefore, the correct answer is **B**.

Descriptive Solution

The correct answer is **B**. Do you notice that the diagram shows a right triangle? The dashed line is the *hypotenuse*—the longest side. The other two sides which form the right angle, labeled 3 km and 4 km, are the *legs*. For all right triangles, the Pythagorean theorem says: *The sum of the squares of the legs equals the square of the hypotenuse.* In the figure above, the sum of the squares of the legs is $3^2 + 4^2 = 9 + 16 = 25$. Therefore, the hypotenuse is the square root of 25, which is 5.

USING MEASUREMENT AND GEOMETRY STANDARDS IN A REAL-LIFE SITUATION

To help you get the "big picture," following are seven Measurement and Geometry standards that are illustrated by an anchor problem called *Paving a Playground*; you might encounter problems such as this after high school. Even though the CAHSEE doesn't include problems with many calculations like this one, you might find it easier to remember one large problem (an "anchor problem"), in which many of the skills are combined, rather than trying to recall how to do each of the standards individually.

Try to do this problem before you look at its solution on the following pages.

Paving a Playground

You work for a paving company and need to give a school a cost estimate for paving the playground and putting a concrete border around its perimeter. A scale drawing of the playground is shown below.

The cost (labor and materials) for the pavement is $54 per square yard.

The cost (labor and materials) for the concrete border is $18 per linear foot.

What's your estimate?

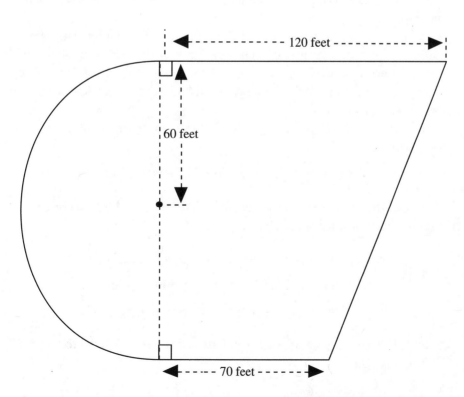

Paving a Playground Solution and Standards

7MG1.2 Construct and read drawings and models made to scale. [1 question]

To begin solving this problem, you'll first need to look at the diagram, read the lengths given, and make decisions about the missing lengths. Let's begin.

Do you see the semicircle, the rectangle, and the triangle? You can use what you know about these shapes plus the numbers given in the scale drawing to find the following lengths: the radius of the circle, and the length and width of the rectangle as shown:

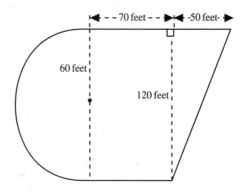

Step 1: Determine the length of the playground's concrete border.

7MG3.3 Know and understand the Pythagorean theorem and its converse and use it to find the length of the missing side of a right triangle and the lengths of other line segments and, in some situations, empirically verify the Pythagorean theorem by direct measurement. [2 questions]

We can use the Pythagorean theorem to find the side of the triangle opposite the right angle (the hypotenuse). The Pythagorean theorem says that for a right triangle, the sum of the squares of the legs gives the square of the hypotenuse. In this figure, the legs are 50 and 120, so you would apply the theorem: $120^2 + 50^2 = 14,400 + 2,500 = 16,900$, which is the square of the hypotenuse. So the square root of 16,900 will be the length of the hypotenuse, <u>130 feet</u>.

Next, you can find the length of the semicircular edge by using the formula for the circumference of a circle. A circle with a radius of 60 feet will have a circumference of $2\pi r$, where $\pi \approx 3.14$. $2\pi r = 2(3.14)60 = 376.8$ ft. But the playground's perimeter includes only half the circumference of the circle, which is 188.4 feet.

7MG2.1 Use formulas routinely for finding the perimeter and area of basic two-dimensional figures and the surface area and volume of basic three-dimensional figures, including rectangles, parallelograms, trapezoids, squares, triangles, circles, prisms and cylinders. [3 questions]

Now you can add up the pieces to find the length of the playground's entire perimeter:

$$50 + 130 + 188.4 + 70 + 70 = 508.4 \text{ feet}$$

Step 2: Find the area of the playground by calculating the areas of the triangle, rectangle, and semi-circle.

Area of triangle is $\frac{1}{2}(50)(120) = 3,000$ square feet.

Area of rectangle is $(70)(120) = 8,400$ square feet.

Area of semicircle is $\frac{1}{2}\pi(60)^2 = 5,652$ square feet.

The sum of these three areas is the total area of the playground to be paved, 17,052 square feet.

Measurement Geometry

Step 3: Figure out the cost of the pavement.

Let's go back to the original problem. What are you asked to find? You need to estimate the cost of paving the playground and its concrete border. Do you see that the cost of pavement and the concrete border are given as rates per unit? Pavement is $54 per square yard, and the border is $18 per linear foot.

Although the cost of pavement is given per square yard, we have calculated the area in square feet! We need to change the square feet into square yards. To do this you will need to use the fact that it takes 9 square feet to make 1 square yard. The area in square feet (17,052) divided by 9 will give the converted area: 1,895 square yards. Finally, you have to multiply the 1,895 square yards by the cost of $54 per square yard to get the final cost of the pavement: $102,330.

Step 4: Figure out the cost of the border.

The only thing left to do is to find the cost of the border. You just need to multiply the perimeter, 508.4 feet, by $18 per linear foot.

508.4($18) = $9,151.

Step 5: Determine the total cost estimate.

If you add the two money amounts together, $102,330 + $9,151, you will have a very good estimate for the work to be done by the paving company: $111,481 (nearest dollar).

Because this is an estimate, you may have rounded numbers off differently and found an estimate close to this. Did you get an estimate between $110,000 and $120,000?

Paving a Playground—Again!

Suppose your company must pave another playground like this one. Could you use the same cost estimate? You could if the two playgrounds were congruent—if both had exactly the same shape and same size.

7MG1.3 Use measures expressed as rates (e.g., speed, density) and measures expressed as products (e.g., person-days) to solve problems; check the units of the solutions; and use dimensional analysis to check the reasonableness of the answer. [2 questions]

7MG1.1 Compare weights capacities, geometric measures, times, and temperatures within and between measurement systems (e.g., miles per hour and feet per second, cubic inches to cubic centimeters). [2 questions]

7MG2.4 Relate the changes in measurement with a change of scale to the units used (e.g., square inches, cubic feet) and to conversions between units (1 square foot = 144 square inches or [1 ft^2] = [144 in^2], 1 cubic inch is approximately 16.38 cubic centimeters. [1 in^3] = [16.38 cm^3]). [1 question]

7MG3.4 Demonstrate an understanding of conditions that indicate two geometrical figures are congruent and what congruence means about the relationships between the sides and angles of the two figures. [1 question]

In order to solve this big problem, you used the math in 7 of the Geometry and Measurement standards. Now you are ready to answer the questions in the next section and then check your answers using the answer key provided in the appendix at the back of this Study Guide.

(Note: The CAHSEE questions used as examples throughout this Study Guide and in the following sample questions were used on prior CAHSEEs. These items will not be used in future CAHSEEs.)

ADDITIONAL MEASUREMENT AND GEOMETRY SAMPLE QUESTIONS

1. **A boy is two meters tall. About how tall is the boy in feet (ft) and inches (in)? (1 meter ≈ 39 inches.)**

   A   5 ft 0 in

   B   5 ft 6 in

   C   6 ft 0 in

   D   6 ft 6 in

   M02044

2. **The actual width (*w*) of a rectangle is 18 centimeters (cm). Use the scale drawing of the rectangle to find the actual length (*l*).**

   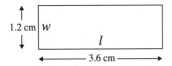

   A   6 cm

   B   24 cm

   C   36 cm

   D   54 cm

   M02087

3. **Beverly ran six miles at the speed of four miles per hour. How long did it take her to run that distance?**

   A $\frac{2}{3}$ hr

   B $1\frac{1}{2}$ hrs

   C   4 hrs

   D   6 hrs

   M02041

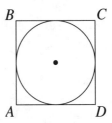

4. **In the figure above, the radius of the inscribed circle is 6 inches (in). What is the perimeter of square *ABCD*?**

   A 12π in

   B 36π in

   C   24 in

   D   48 in

   M02236

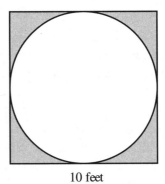

10 feet

5. **The largest possible circle is to be cut from a 10-foot square board. What will be the approximate area, in square feet, of the remaining board (shaded region)?**
   $\left(A = \pi r^2 \text{ and } \pi \approx 3.14\right)$

   A   20

   B   30

   C   50

   D   80

   M00404

6. A right triangle is removed from a rectangle as shown in the figure below. Find the area of the remaining part of the rectangle.

$$\left(\text{Area of a triangle} = \frac{1}{2}bh \right)$$

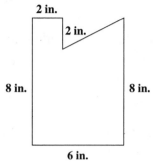

2 in.

2 in.

8 in.   8 in.

6 in.

A   40 in.²

B   44 in.²

C   48 in.²

D   52 in.²

M02093

7. The short stairway shown below is made of solid concrete. The height and width of each step is 10 inches (in.). The length is 20 inches.

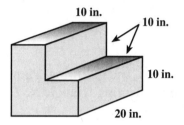

10 in.

10 in.

10 in.

20 in.

What is the volume, in cubic inches, of the concrete used to create this stairway?

A   3000

B   4000

C   6000

D   8000

M02990

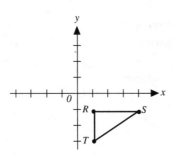

8.   Which of the following triangles *R′S′T′* is the image of triangle *RST* that results from reflecting triangle *RST* across the *y*-axis?

A

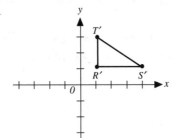

C

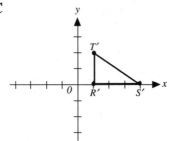

B

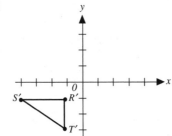

D

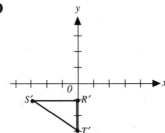

M02861

9.   What is the value of *x* in the right triangle shown below?

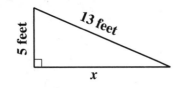

A   8 feet

B   12 feet

C   18 feet

D   23 feet

M03181

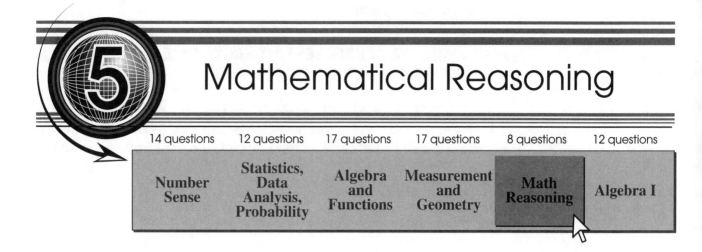

Mathematical Reasoning

14 questions	12 questions	17 questions	17 questions	8 questions	12 questions
Number Sense	Statistics, Data Analysis, Probability	Algebra and Functions	Measurement and Geometry	Math Reasoning	Algebra I

Eight of the 80 CAHSEE multiple-choice questions are based on 6 selected standards from the grade 7 Mathematical Reasoning strand. Each Mathematical Reasoning question used on the CAHSEE is also linked to one of the other strands. When CAHSEE results are reported to students and parents, the Mathematical Reasoning results are not reported separately; instead, the results are reported under the linked strand.

WHAT DO THE MATHEMATICAL REASONING STANDARDS ASK ME TO DO?

"Mathematical Reasoning" includes the logical thinking skills that you develop while learning mathematics and can carry over into other disciplines.

The Mathematical Reasoning strand includes:
- recognizing and generalizing patterns
- identifying and organizing relevant information
- validating conjectures both inductively and deductively

WHY IS MATHEMATICAL REASONING IMPORTANT?

After high school, you'll need to find answers to questions such as these:

- Where should I live?
- What college should I go to?
- What kind of work matches my aspirations and skills?

How do people make such important life decisions? Some people make many decisions based entirely on intuition and emotion. But often, better decisions can be made by gathering facts, asking for advice, and considering the consequences of choosing various options. This kind of thinking—reasoning from known facts to reach a logical conclusion—is central to mathematics and is essential for successful problem solving in almost all aspects of adult life.

HOW WILL THE CAHSEE TEST MY KNOWLEDGE OF MATHEMATICAL REASONING?

The CAHSEE tests 6 of the 14 grade 7 standards from the Mathematical Reasoning strand. To illustrate how the Mathematical Reasoning standards are tested, we'll look at three sample CAHSEE questions from this strand.

7MR1.1 Analyze problems by identifying relationships, distinguishing relevant from irrelevant information, identifying missing information, sequencing and prioritizing information, and observing patterns. [2 questions]

Sample CAHSEE Question

A flower shop delivery van traveled these distances during one week: 104.4, 117.8, 92.3, 168.7, and 225.6 miles. How many gallons of gas were used by the delivery van during this week?

What other information is needed in order to solve this problem?

A the average speed traveled in miles per hour

B the cost of gasoline per gallon

C the average number of miles per gallon for the van

D the number of different deliveries the van made

M00138

Mathematical Solution	*Descriptive Solution*
• The correct answer is **C**. Please refer to the next column for a description of the solution.	Adding the five numbers gives you the total miles the van was driven during the whole week. But how much gasoline was used? We need more information. If we knew how many miles the van could travel on one gallon of gas—miles per gallon—we could find the gallons used by dividing the total miles traveled by the number of miles per gallon. Which of the four choices gives information about gallons of gasoline and miles traveled? Choice **C**, "The average number of miles per gallon for the van," is what you need. (This Mathematical Reasoning question is linked to Algebra and Functions standard 7AF1.1.)

Mathematical Reasoning

7MR1.2 Formulate and justify mathematical conjectures based on a general description of the mathematical question or problem posed. [1 question]

Sample CAHSEE Question

If n is any odd number, which of the following is true about $n+1$?

A It is an odd number.

B It is an even number.

C It is a prime number.

D It is the same number as $n-1$.

M00155

Mathematical Solution

- The correct answer is **B**. Please refer to the next column for a description of the solution.

Descriptive Solution

Every whole number is either odd or even. A whole number is even if it can be divided evenly by two; the numbers 2, 4, 6, 8, 10, 12, . . . are even. In this question we are given the information that n is an odd number. Because n is odd, it must be one of the numbers 1, 3, 5, 7, 9, 11, 13, 15, and so on. Now we have to reason mathematically. If n is a member of this "odd" list, then what can we say for sure about $n+1$? If we add 1 to each number in the odd list, we get the "$n+1$" list: 2, 4, 6, 8, 10, 12, 14, 16, and so on, which are even numbers. Therefore, the correct answer is **B** because the "$n+1$" list consists of only even numbers. (This Mathematical Reasoning question is also linked to Algebra and Functions standard 7AF1.1.)

7MR3.3 Develop generalizations of the results obtained and the strategies used and apply them to new problem situations. [1 question]

Sample CAHSEE Question

> Len runs a mile in 8 minutes. At this rate how long will it take him to run a 26-mile marathon?

Which of the following problems can be solved using the same arithmetic operations that are used to solve the problem above?

A Len runs 26 miles in 220 minutes. How long does it take him to run each mile?

B A librarian has 356 books to place on 18 shelves. Each shelf will contain the same number of books. How many books can the librarian place on each shelf?

C A cracker box weighs 200 grams. What is the weight of 100 boxes?

D Each basket of strawberries weighs 60 grams. How many baskets can be filled from 500 grams of strawberries?

M00137

Mathematical Solution

- The correct answer is **C**. Please refer to the next column for a description of the solution.

Descriptive Solution

Often the same mathematical idea or skill can apply in very different situations. That's what you have to do in this problem. The correct answer is **C**. Here is why. In the original problem, Len runs one mile in 8 minutes, so you'd have to multiply 8 by 26 to get the minutes it would take him to run the 26 miles at the same rate. The arithmetic operation used to solve this problem is multiplication. Which of the choices, A, B, C, or D, requires multiplication?

In choice A, you'd have to divide the 220 minutes by 26 to get the time for one mile. For choice B, the total number of books would have to be divided by the number of shelves to get the books per shelf. Finally, in choice D, to find the number of baskets you'd have to divide the 500 grams by 60. But to figure out choice C, the weight of one box of crackers, 200 grams, would have to be multiplied by 100 to find the weight of all the boxes. Only in choice **C** would you have to multiply, as in the original problem. (This Mathematical Reasoning question is also linked to Number Sense standard 7NS1.2.)

Mathematical Reasoning

Here are the other three Mathematical Reasoning standards tested on the CAHSEE:

7MR2.1 Use estimation to verify the reasonableness of calculated results. [2 questions]

7MR2.3 Estimate unknown quantities graphically and solve for them by using logical reasoning and arithmetic and algebraic techniques. [1 question]

7MR2.4 Make and test conjectures by using both inductive and deductive reasoning. [1 question]

In the sample questions that follow, questions 2, 3, and 4 are based on these three Mathematical Reasoning standards, respectively.

Now try out your Mathematical Reasoning skills by doing the sample questions. Check your answers using the answer key provided in the appendix at the back of this Study Guide.

(Note: The CAHSEE questions used as examples throughout this Study Guide and in the following sample questions were used on prior CAHSEEs. These items will not be used in future CAHSEEs.)

ADDITIONAL MATHEMATICAL REASONING SAMPLE QUESTIONS

1. **Chris drove 100 kilometers from San Francisco to Santa Cruz in 2 hours and 30 minutes. What computation will give Chris' average speed, in kilometers per hour?**

   A Divide 100 by 2.5.

   B Divide 100 by 2.3.

   C Multiply 100 by 2.5.

   D Multiply 100 by 2.3.

   M03164

2. **Which is the BEST estimate of 326 • 279 ?**

   A 900

   B 9,000

   C 90,000

   D 900,000

   M00277

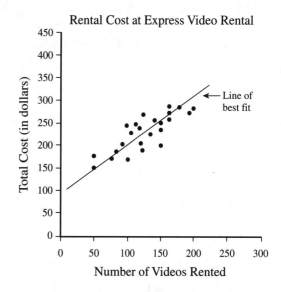

Rental Cost at Express Video Rental

3. **Using the line of best fit shown on the scatterplot above, which of the following BEST approximates the rental cost per video to rent 300 videos?**

   A $3.00

   B $2.50

   C $2.00

   D $1.50

   M02209

Mathematical Reasoning

4. The winning number in a contest
    was less than 50. It was a multiple of
    3, 5, and 6. What was the number?

    A 14

    B 15

    C 30

    D It cannot be determined.

    M00393

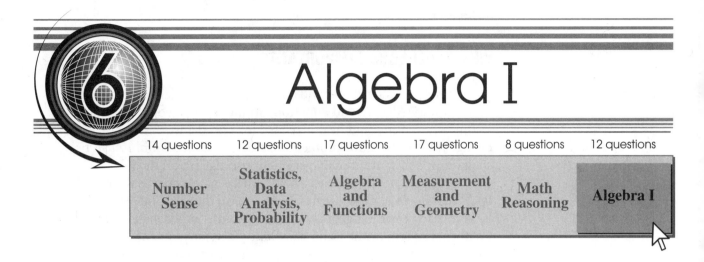

Algebra I

14 questions   12 questions   17 questions   17 questions   8 questions   12 questions

| Number Sense | Statistics, Data Analysis, Probability | Algebra and Functions | Measurement and Geometry | Math Reasoning | Algebra I |

Twelve of the 80 CAHSEE multiple-choice questions are based on 10 of the Algebra I standards.

WHAT DO THE ALGEBRA I STANDARDS ASK ME TO DO?

To answer the CAHSEE Algebra I questions, you'll need to know how to:

- recognize equivalent forms of polynomials and other algebraic expressions
- understand the meaning of *opposite, reciprocal, root,* and *absolute value*
- identify the graph that matches a particular linear function and find its slope and intercepts
- know that lines on a graph are parallel if and only if they have the same slope
- solve linear inequalities
- solve problems involving rate, average speed, distance, and time
- identify the solution to a system of two equations in two unknowns
- solve classic algebra rate, work, and percent mixture problems

Vocabulary

The words below have appeared on the CAHSEE during past administrations. If any of these words are unfamiliar to you, look them up in the CAHSEE Math Vocabulary list in the appendix at the back of this Study Guide, or check with your math teacher.

absolute value   slope of a line   *y*-intercept

parallel   *x*-intercept

Algebra I

WHY IS ALGEBRA I IMPORTANT?

The Algebra I standards expand and deepen basic algebra skills included in the grade 7 Algebra and Functions strand. Many people working in technical, scientific, and health-related jobs need a working knowledge of Algebra I. The anchor problem for this strand, *Restaurant Advertising*, shows how a restaurant manager might use algebra on the job.

In the U.S. today, algebra has become a "gatekeeper" subject even in fields that don't actually use much algebra on the job. The reality nowadays is "if you don't know algebra, you don't get into either the University of California system or the California State University system." Knowing the basics of algebra enables you to keep your future options open.

HOW WILL THE CAHSEE TEST MY KNOWLEDGE OF ALGEBRA I?

The CAHSEE tests 10 of the 29 standards from the Algebra I strand. Let's start by looking at 5 of these standards and some actual CAHSEE questions based on them. Each box that follows contains one of the standards, a sample question based on that standard, and a solution with an explanation.

1A2.0 Students understand and use such operations as taking the opposite, finding the reciprocal, and taking a root, ~~and raising to a fractional power~~. They understand and use the rules of exponents. [1 question] (Note: The crossed out portion will not be tested on the CAHSEE.)

Sample CAHSEE Question

If $x = -7$, then $-x =$

A -7

B $-\dfrac{1}{7}$

C $\dfrac{1}{7}$

D 7

M02863

Mathematical Solution

- From the given information, substitute x with -7.

- $-x = -(-7) = 7$

- Therefore, the correct answer is **D**: 7.

Descriptive Solution

The correct answer is **D**. If $x = -7$, then $-x = 7$, because "$-x$" means "take the opposite of x." Because $x = -7$, the opposite of -7 is 7. Number pairs that are opposites add to 0; therefore, the opposite of -7 is 7 because $-7 + 7 = 0$.

Number pairs that are reciprocals multiply to give 1. For example, 7 and $\dfrac{1}{7}$ are reciprocals because $7\left(\dfrac{1}{7}\right) = 1$. Choice B is incorrect; it is the reciprocal of -7.

Algebra I

1A3.0 Students solve equations and inequalities involving absolute values. [1 question]

Sample CAHSEE Question

If x is an integer, what is the solution to $|x-3|<1$?

A $\{-3\}$

B $\{-3, -2, -1, 0, 1\}$

C $\{3\}$

D $\{-1, 0, 1, 2, 3\}$

M03035

Mathematical Solution

- $|x-3|<1 \rightarrow$

Solve:
$$\begin{array}{r} x-3 < 1 \\ +3 \quad +3 \\ \hline x < 4 \end{array}$$

and solve:
$$\begin{array}{r} x-3 > -1 \\ +3 \quad +3 \\ \hline x > 2 \end{array}$$

- So, $2 < x < 4$; therefore, the correct answer is **C**.

Descriptive Solution

Let's test the numbers in each set of x-values to see if they make $|x-3|<1$ true. Check choice A by putting in -3 for x. Is $|-3-3|<1$? No, it is not, because $|-3-3| = |-6| = 6$, and 6 is not less than 1, so choice A is wrong. Also, you now know choice B is incorrect, because -3, which made choice A incorrect, is in the set of choice B.

Next let's try choice C. If x is 3 then $|x-3| = |3-3| = |0| = 0$. Because $0 < 1$, choice C could be the answer, but we still need to check to see if choice D might be even better. Try letting x be -1 first. Then $|x-3| = |-1-3| = |-4| = 4$. But 4 is not less than 1. So D cannot be the answer. Therefore, the correct answer is **C**.

Another way to analyze this problem is to use the fact that the absolute value of a number is the number's distance from 0 on the number line. So, if the absolute value of $x-3$ is to be less than or equal to 1, then $x-3$ must be between -1 and 1. This gives two inequalities: $-1 < x-3$ and $x-3 < 1$. Solving each of these inequalities you get that $2 < x$ and $x < 4$. So, x must lie between 2 and 4. The only integer that is both greater than 2 and less than 4 is 3. So, the correct solution set is $\{3\}$.

1A4.0 Students simplify expressions before solving linear equations and inequalities in one variable, such as $3(2x\text{-}5) + 4(x\text{-}2) = 12$. [2 questions]

Sample CAHSEE Question

Which equation is equivalent to $\dfrac{x+3}{8} = \dfrac{2x-1}{5}$?

A $5x+3=16x-1$

B $5x+15=16x-8$

C $8x+3=10x-1$

D $8x+24=10x-5$

M13117

Mathematical Solution

- Multiply the left and right sides of the equation by 8 so that it cancels.

$$\frac{8(x+3)}{8} = \frac{8(2x-1)}{5}$$

$$x+3 = \frac{16x-8}{5}$$

- Multiply the left and right sides of the equation by 5 so that it cancels.

$$5(x+3) = \frac{5(16x-8)}{5}$$

$$5x+15 = 16x-8$$

Therefore, the correct answer is **B**.

Descriptive Solution

Multiply the left and right sides of the equation first by 8 and then by 5, so that the equation will no longer contain fractions. When multiplying the 8 and then the 5, be sure to distribute these numbers to each term in the equation. Therefore, the correct answer is **B**.

1A6.0 Students graph a linear equation and compute the *x*- and *y*-intercepts (e.g., graph 2*x* + 6*y* = 4). ~~They are also able to sketch the region defined by linear inequality (e.g., they sketch the region defined by 2*x* + 6*y* < 4).~~ **[1 graphing item; 1 computing item]** (Note: The crossed out portion will not be tested on the CAHSEE.)

Sample CAHSEE Question

Which of the following is the graph of $y = \dfrac{1}{2}x + 2$?

A

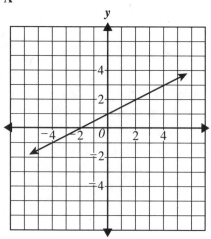

C

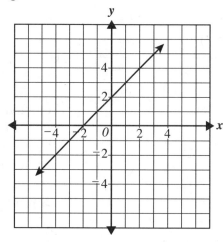

B

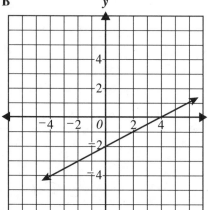

D

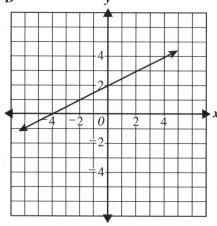

M02026

1A6.0 Sample CAHSEE Question cont'd	
Mathematical Solution • The correct answer is **D**. Please refer to the next column for a description of the solution.	*Descriptive Solution* Notice that the equation $y = \frac{1}{2}x + 2$ is in "slope-intercept form" for linear equations where the slope is $\frac{1}{2}$ and the y-intercept is at 2. Which graphs have a slope of $\frac{1}{2}$? In a graph we can find the slope by looking at the ratio "rise over run." If we pick any two points on the line, we can look at the vertical and horizontal changes to find the slope: 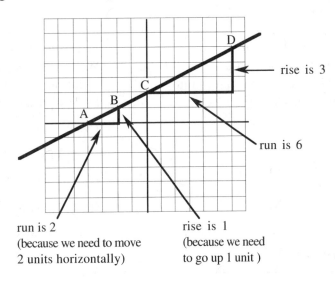 To move from point A to point B on the line, the ratio of rise to run is $\frac{1}{2}$. For a line, the slope ratio always reduces to the same fraction, no matter which two points are selected. To move from point C to point D on the line, the ratio of rise to run is $\frac{3}{6}$, which still equals $\frac{1}{2}$. Looking back at the answers to this CAHSEE question, you can see that graphs A, B, and D all have slopes of $\frac{1}{2}$. But graph C has a slope of 1, so we know it is not the correct answer. Next we need to look for the correct y-intercept. Which graph has a y-intercept of 2? Not graph A; its y-intercept is at 1. Nor graph B; its y-intercept is at -2. But graph D does have a y-intercept of 2. Therefore, the correct answer is **D**.

Algebra I

1A7.0 Students verify that a point lies on a line, given an equation of the line. Students are able to derive linear equations ~~by using the point slope formula.~~ [1 question] (Note: The crossed out portion will not be tested on the CAHSEE.)

Sample CAHSEE Question

Which of the following points lies on the line $4x + 5y = 20$?

A $(0, 4)$

B $(0, 5)$

C $(4, 5)$

D $(5, 4)$

M02565

Mathematical Solution	*Descriptive Solution*
• Start with the first point $(0, 4)$ and substitute x and y values into the equation $4x + 5y = 20$.	We can test each point's coordinates in the equation $4x + 5y = 20$ and see which one works. Let's start with choice D and work backwards.
$$4(0) + 5(4) = 20$$ $$0 + 20 = 20$$ $$20 = 20$$	$(5, 4)$ Does $4(5) + 5(4) = 20$? No. $(4, 5)$ Does $4(4) + 5(5) = 20$? No. $(0, 5)$ Does $4(0) + 5(5) = 20$? No. $(0, 4)$ Does $4(0) + 5(4) = 20$? Yes! So the correct answer is **A**.
• Yes! Therefore, the correct answer is **A**.	

1A8.0 Students understand the concepts of parallel lines ~~and perpendicular lines~~ and how their slopes are related. ~~Students are able to find the equation of a line perpendicular to a given line that passes through a given point.~~ [1 question] (Note: The crossed out portion will not be tested on the CAHSEE.)

Sample CAHSEE Question

Which of the following could be the equation of a line parallel to the line $y = 4x - 7$?

A $\quad y = \dfrac{1}{4}x - 7$

B $\quad y = 4x + 3$

C $\quad y = -4x + 3$

D $\quad y = -\dfrac{1}{4}x - 7$

M02651

Mathematical Solution

- The correct answer is **B**. Please refer to the next column for a description of the solution.

Descriptive Solution

Parallel lines must have the same slope. The equation given to us, $y = 4x - 7$, is in slope-intercept form with a slope of 4. The four possible answer choices are also in slope-intercept form. Notice that only the equation of choice B has a slope of 4. Choice **B** is the only equation whose graph is parallel to $y = 4x - 7$, making it the correct answer.

Algebra I

1A9.0 Students solve a system of two linear equations in two variables algebraically and are able to interpret the answer graphically. Students are able to solve a system of two linear inequalities in two variables and to sketch the solution sets. [1 question]

Sample CAHSEE Question

$$\begin{cases} y = 3x - 5 \\ y = 2x \end{cases}$$

What is the solution of the system of equations shown above?

A $(1, -2)$

B $(1, 2)$

C $(5, 10)$

D $(-5, -10)$

M02649

Mathematical Solution

- We can solve this system of equations using the substitution method and solving for x first. Since both equations are equal to y, set them equal to each other.

$$y = 3x - 5 \text{ and } y = 2x$$
$$\text{therefore, } 3x - 5 = 2x$$

- Solve the resulting equation for x.

$$\begin{array}{r} 3x - 5 = 2x \\ -2x \qquad -2x \\ \hline x - 5 = 0 \\ +5 +5 \\ \hline x = 5 \end{array}$$

- Now substitute $x = 5$ for one (or both) of the given equations and solve for y.

$$y = 3x - 5 \rightarrow y = 3(5) - 5 \rightarrow y = 15 - 5 \rightarrow y = 10$$

or $y = 2x \rightarrow y = 2(5) \rightarrow y = 10$

So $(5, 10)$ is the solution to the system.
Therefore, the correct answer is **C**.

Descriptive Solution

We can solve this system of equations using the substitution method and solving for x first. Since both equations are given in terms of y, set them equal to each other. The resulting equation is $3x - 5 = 2x$. Solving for x, you get $x = 5$. In order to find the y-value, substitute $x = 5$ for one or both equations and solve for y. So,

$$y = 3x - 5 \rightarrow y = 3(5) - 5 \rightarrow$$
$$y = 15 - 5 \rightarrow y = 10 \text{ or}$$
$$y = 2x \rightarrow y = 2(5) \rightarrow y = 10.$$

The result is the ordered pair $(5, 10)$. Therefore, the correct answer is **C**.

1A10.0 Students add, subtract, multiply, and divide monomials and polynomials. Students solve multistep problems, including word problems, by using these techniques. [1 question]

Sample CAHSEE Question

Simplify.

$$\frac{4x^3 + 2x^2 - 8x}{2x}$$

A $2x^2 + x - 4$

B $4x^2 + 2x - 8$

C $2x^2 + 2x^2 - 8x$

D $8x^4 + 4x^3 - 16x^2$

M03354

Mathematical Solution

- In order to simplify, divide each term in the numerator by the denominator.

$$\frac{4x^3 + 2x^2 - 8x}{2x} \rightarrow \frac{4x^3}{2x} + \frac{2x^2}{2x} - \frac{8x}{2x} \rightarrow$$

- Using exponent rules,

$$2x^{3-1} + x^{2-1} - 4x^{1-1} \rightarrow 2x^2 + x^1 - 4x^0 \rightarrow$$

$$2x^2 + x - 4$$

Therefore, the correct answer is **A**.

Descriptive Solution

In order to simplify, divide each term in the numerator by the denominator. Since this item contains exponents, be sure to apply the rules of exponents correctly. In order to start, you may rewrite the expression as $\frac{4x^3}{2x} + \frac{2x^2}{2x} - \frac{8x}{2x}$. Next, divide the coefficient and exponent of each term. This will result in $2x^{3-1} + x^{2-1} - 4x^{1-1}$. Don't forget to simplify the exponents as well. The result is $2x^2 + x^1 - 4x^0$. Only a few more exponent rules to remember: $x^1 = x$ and $x^0 = 1$. Simplifying this, you get $2x^2 + x - 4$. Therefore, the correct answer is **A**.

Algebra I

1A15.0 Students apply algebraic techniques to solve rate problems, work problems, and percent mixture problems. [1 question]

Sample CAHSEE Question

Diane delivers newspapers for $5 a day plus $0.04 per newspaper delivered. Jeremy delivers newspapers for $2 a day plus $0.10 per newspaper delivered. How many newspapers would Diane and Jeremy each need to deliver in order to earn the same amount?

A   30

B   50

C   75

D   83

M02614

Mathematical Solution

- Write an equation based on what was given and set them equal to each other, since we are looking for them to earn the same amount. Let *n* equal the number of newspapers they each need to deliver.

  $$\$5 + \$0.04n = \$2 + \$0.10n$$

- Solve the equation for *n*.

$$\$5 + \$0.04n = \$2 + \$0.10n$$
$$\underline{-\$2 \qquad\qquad -\$2}$$
$$\$3 + \$0.04n = \qquad \$0.10n$$
$$\underline{-\$0.04n \qquad -\$0.04n}$$
$$\frac{\$3}{\$0.06} = \frac{\$0.06n}{\$0.06}$$
$$50 = n$$

Therefore, the correct answer is **B**.

Descriptive Solution

We must first analyze the question to see what is being asked. We need to find out how many newspapers that Diane and Jeremy each need to deliver in order to earn the same amount. We will need to set up expressions based on what is given and set these expressions equal to each other to create an equation. Since we are looking for the number of newspapers, we need to create a variable for our equations. Let's name our variable *n*, since it stands for the number of newspapers. The expression for Diane will be $\$5 + \$0.04n$, since she gets paid $5 a day plus $0.04 for each newspaper she delivers. The expression for Jeremy will be $\$2 + \$0.10n$, since he gets paid $2 a day plus $0.10 for each newspaper he delivers.

Now that we have the expressions, let's set them equal to each other so that we can find the number of newspapers they need to deliver to earn the same amount.

$$\$5 + \$0.04n = \$2 + \$0.10n$$

In order to solve for *n*, we should first subtract $2 from both sides of the equation and then $0.04 from both sides of the equation so that we can get *n* on one side. We should then divide each side of the equation by $0.06 to get *n* on one side.

$$\frac{\$3}{\$0.06} = \frac{\$0.06n}{\$0.06}$$

The result is $n = 50$. Therefore, the correct answer is **B**.

Algebra I

USING ALGEBRA I STANDARDS IN A REAL-LIFE SITUATION

The remaining 2 Algebra I standards are illustrated by a real-life problem, *Restaurant Advertising*.

Try to do this problem before you look at its solution.

Restaurant Advertising

The manager of a restaurant has a total of $725 to spend on advertising. The advertisement for the restaurant will be a copy of the menu that costs $0.50 each to print. The manager will pay a total of $250 for an employee to distribute the advertisements in different parts of the city. Based on this information, how many total menus can be printed so that the manager spends exactly $725?

Restaurant Advertising Solution and Standards

Step 1: Write an equation based on the given information.

Now we can create an equation based on the information we were given. The question is asking us to find the total menus that can be printed, so we can let m represent the number of total menus.

Each menu costs $0.50 to print so we will need to multiply that by the total number of menus, m in this case. We must also remember that it is going to cost $250 to pay an employee to distribute the menus. The total amount the manager can spend is $725 so,

$$\$0.50m + \$250 = \$725$$

Step 2: Solve the equation for m.

$$\$0.50m + \$250 = \$725$$

Subtract $250 from both sides of the equation.

$$
\begin{array}{r}
\$0.50m + \$250 = \$725 \\
-\$250 \quad -\$250 \\
\hline
\$0.50m \qquad = \$475
\end{array}
$$

Continue, to solve for m.

$$\$0.50m = \$475$$

7AF1.1 Use variables and appropriate operations to write an expression, an equation, an inequality, or a system of equations or inequalities that represents a verbal description (e.g., three less than a number, half as large as area A). [2 questions]

1A2.0 Students understand and use such operations as taking the opposite, finding the reciprocal, and taking a root, ~~and raising to a fractional power~~. They understand and use the rules of exponents. [1 question]

Algebra I

1A5.0 Students solve multistep problems, including word problems, involving linear equations and linear inequalities in one variable and provide justification for each step. [1 question]

Divide both sides of the equation by $0.50.

$$\frac{\$0.50m}{\$0.50} = \frac{\$475}{\$0.50}$$

$$m = 950$$

So, the manager can have 950 menus printed for $0.50 each and pay an employee $250 to distribute the menus for a total of $725.

Now that you've read about all the Algebra I standards, it is time to answer the questions in the next section and then check your answers using the answer key provided in the appendix at the back of this Study Guide.

(Note: The CAHSEE questions used as examples throughout this Study Guide are questions that were used on prior CAHSEEs. These items will not be used in future CAHSEEs.)

ADDITIONAL ALGEBRA I SAMPLE QUESTIONS

1. The perimeter, P, of a square may be found by using the formula $\left(\dfrac{1}{4}\right)P = \sqrt{A}$, where A is the area of the square. What is the perimeter of the square with an area of 36 square inches?

   A   9 inches
   B   12 inches
   C   24 inches
   D   72 inches

   M00057

2. Assume y is an integer and solve for y.

   $$|y+2| = 9$$

   A   {–11, 7}
   B   {–7, 7}
   C   {–7, 11}
   D   {–11, 11}

   M02242

3. Which of the following is equivalent to $4(x+5) - 3(x+2) = 14$?

   A $4x + 20 - 3x - 6 = 14$
   B $4x + 5 - 3x + 6 = 14$
   C $4x + 5 - 3x + 2 = 14$
   D $4x + 20 - 3x - 2 = 14$

   M02936

4. Solve for x.

   $$5(2x-3) - 6x < 9$$

   A $x < -1.5$
   B $x < 1.5$
   C $x < 3$
   D $x < 6$

   M02938

5. What is the y-intercept of the line $2x - 3y = 12$?

   A $(0,-4)$
   B $(0,-3)$
   C $(2,0)$
   D $(6,0)$

   M02591

6. What is the slope of a line parallel to the line $y = \dfrac{1}{3}x + 2$?

   A -3
   B $-\dfrac{1}{3}$
   C $\dfrac{1}{3}$
   D 2

   M02565

ADDITIONAL ALGEBRA I SAMPLE QUESTIONS

$$\begin{cases} 7x + 3y = -8 \\ -4x - y = 6 \end{cases}$$

7. **What is the solution to the system of equations shown above?**

    A $(-2, -2)$

    B $(-2, 2)$

    C $(2, -2)$

    D $(2, 2)$

    M02956

8. **Mr. Jacobs can correct 150 quizzes in 50 minutes. His student aide can correct 150 quizzes in 75 minutes. Working together, how many minutes will it take them to correct 150 quizzes?**

    A   30

    B   60

    C   63

    D   125

    M03000

CAHSEE Mathematics Vocabulary and Answer Key

CAHSEE MATHEMATICS VOCABULARY

Absolute value is the distance of a number from zero on the number line. The distance is always positive or equal to zero. The symbol for absolute value consists of two vertical bars | | with a numerical value in between.

Example: | −5 | and | 5 | are both 5 because the distance from −5 to 0 is 5 units and from 5 to 0 is 5 units.

Spanish words with the same meaning as *absolute value*: valor absoluto

---

Area is the measurement of a surface, expressed in square units. The surface of your desktop has area; so does the state of California. The area of the desktop can be given in square inches or square feet; the area of the state of California is approximately 158,868 square miles. The areas of some shapes can be found by measuring lengths and using a formula. Below are the shapes and area formulas you'll need to know for the CAHSEE.

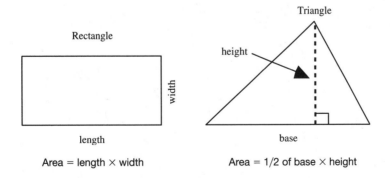

Rectangle

width

length

Area = length × width

Triangle

height

base

Area = 1/2 of base × height

Spanish word with the same meaning as *area:* área

Bar graph refers to a way of displaying data using horizontal or vertical bars. The bars represent quantities (i.e., the longer the bar, the greater the quantity).

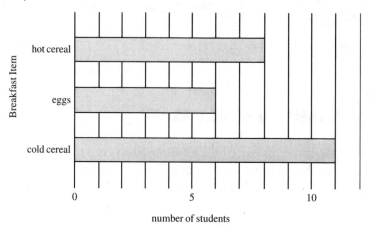

What Mrs. Garcia's students had for breakfast

In Mrs. Garcia's class, five more students had cold cereal than had eggs for breakfast.

Spanish words with the same meaning as *bar graph*: gráfica de barras

A **circle** is a plane figure consisting of all points at a given distance (the radius) from a single point (the center). This diagram shows some of the vocabulary words used with the circle.

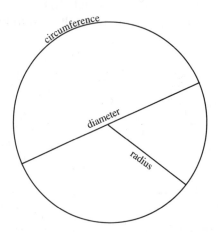

A **diameter** is a line segment that joins two points on the circle and passes through the center.

A **radius** is a line segment that joins the center of a circle with a point on the circle. For any circle, the length of a radius is always half the length of a diameter.

The **circumference** of a circle is the length all the way around a circle. For every circle, the ratio of the length around (circumference) to the length across (diameter) is a little more than three. The exact value of this ratio, 3.14159 . . . , is called *pi*, and is usually written as the Greek alphabet character π. The formula for the circumference of a circle is $C = \pi d$ where d is the diameter. Also, because the diameter is twice the length of a radius, $C = \pi d = 2\pi r$

Spanish word that has the same meaning as *circle*: círculo

———————

Compound interest: When you have a savings account, the bank pays you for the use of your money. This payment is called interest. When the term compound interest is used, it means that the interest is calculated by finding the product of the original amount of money, the interest rate, and the time the money is in the bank before more interest is added to the previous amount of money in the bank.

For example, suppose you put $500 in a bank that pays 5% interest per year for 2 years that is compounded. If you make no additional deposits or withdrawals, the interest for the first year is calculated by $500 • 0.05 • 1 = $25. When you add the $25 to your original amount, you now have $525 in the bank. As before, if you do not make any additional deposits or withdrawals, the interest for the second year will be calculated based on the amount of money in the bank after the first year, $525 • 0.05 • 1 = $26.25. When you add the $26.25 to the $525 in the bank, you now have $551.25.

Spanish words with the same meaning as *compound interest*: interés compuesto

———————

Congruent: Two shapes are congruent if they can be placed one on top of the other and all points match. This means that all matching lengths and all matching angles are the same size.

Spanish word with the same meaning as *congruent*: congruente

———————

Correlation is a way of measuring how closely related two sets of paired data are to one another. The correlation may be positive, negative, or none—that is, there may be no correlation between two data sets. One way of seeing correlation is to plot the data in a scatterplot and look for a pattern.

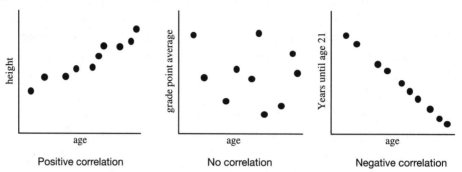

There is a *positive correlation* of student height to student age; the scatterplot shows that for this group, as the students' ages increase, their heights also increase. Between student ages and student grades there appears to be no correlation; the points have no apparent pattern.

There is a *negative correlation* between the students' ages now and the number of years until they are 21: the older they are, the fewer the number of years until they are 21.

Spanish word with the same meaning as *correlation*: correlación

———————

Decreased by means to make a quantity smaller by a certain number. If Marco weighs 150 pounds and he decreases his weight by 10 pounds, then he now weighs 140 pounds.

Spanish words with the same meaning as *decreased by*: disminuída por

———————

Dependent events (See *Independent events*.)

Spanish words with the same meaning as *dependent events*: eventos dependientes

———————

The **diameter** is a segment in a circle that goes through the center of the circle and meets the circumference at each end. (See *circle*.)

Spanish word with the same meaning as *diameter*: diámetro

Equivalent expressions are numerical expressions that have the same value, or, if the expression contains variables, result in the same values for every value of the variable.

For example, $\frac{1}{4}$ is equivalent to 0.25 or $\frac{2}{8}$ or 25% or $\frac{4}{16}$ because all these expressions are the same number value.

Two algebraic expressions are equivalent if they always result in the same number value when the same numbers are substituted for the variable(s).

For example, "$5(x + y - 2)$" is equivalent to "$5x + 5y - 10$."

To see this, suppose 3 is put in for x and 4 is put in for y.

Then $\underline{5(x + y - 2)} = 5(3 + 4 - 2) = 5(5) = 25$

And $\underline{5x + 5y - 10} = 5(3) + 5(4) - 10 = 15 + 20 - 10 = 25$

In fact, the distributive property tells us that these two expressions give the same number as output, no matter what values of x and y are put in.

Sometimes on multiple-choice tests, you can quickly get an idea whether two expressions are equivalent by checking the values of the expressions for a few specific numbers. This tactic is especially useful for finding out when expressions are <u>not</u> equivalent. If you put the same numbers in for the variables in two expressions, but different numbers are output, then you know the two expressions are not equivalent.

For example, suppose on a multiple-choice test the question is "$(x + y)^2$ is equivalent to:" and one of the possible answers is "$x^2 + y^2$." You could check to see whether these expressions are equivalent by trying 3 for x and 4 for y: Then $(x + y)^2 = (3 + 4)^2 = 7^2 = \mathbf{49}$. But $x^2 + y^2 = 3^2 + 4^2 = 9 + 16 = \mathbf{25}$. Because the two expressions give different output numbers for the same input numbers, they are not equivalent.

<u>Equations or inequalities are equivalent</u> if they have exactly the same solution set. For example, $4(x + 5) - 3(x + 2) = 14$ and $4x + 20 - 6x - 6 = 14$ are equivalent because both equations are true if and only if $x = 0$.

Spanish words with the same meaning as *equivalent equations*: ecuaciones equivalentes

---

Expression refers to a number, a variable, or a combination of variables, numbers and symbols. $16x^2$ and $3x + 4y$ and $25t$ and $8^{3/2}$ are all expressions.

Spanish word with the same meaning as *expression*: expresión

The **hypotenuse** in a right triangle is the side opposite the right angle. The Pythagorean theorem for right triangles is sometimes given as "$a^2 + b^2 = c^2$." In this formula, the a^2 and b^2 are the squares of the legs and the c^2 refers to the length of the hypotenuse squared.

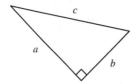

Hypotenuse and right angle

Spanish word with the same meaning as *hypotenuse*: hipotenusa

Independent events, dependent events: These terms are used when figuring probabilities. In probability, an *event* is a particular happening that may or may not occur. Some examples of events are: "A fair coin will come up heads on the next flip," and "Rain will fall in Oakland tomorrow," and "Trudy Trimble will win next week's California lottery."

One event is said to be *independent* of another if the first event can occur with absolutely no effect on the probability of the second event's happening. For example, suppose you are going to flip a fair coin two times and on the first flip it comes up heads. On the second flip, the probability of the coin coming up heads is still 50%. Each flip of the coin is *independent* of all other flips.

But some events are *dependent;* that is, the probability of one event depends on whether the other event occurs. For example, suppose you are randomly choosing two marbles, one after another, from a bag that contains three blue marbles and three red marbles. On your first draw, you have a 50% chance of drawing a blue marble. But on your second draw, the probability of drawing a blue marble depends on which color you pulled out on the first draw. The probability of getting a blue marble on your second draw is *dependent* upon the result of the first draw.

Spanish words with the same meaning as *independent events, dependent events:* eventos independientes, eventos dependientes

Integers are the set of whole numbers and their opposites:
$\{ \ldots -3, -2, -1, 0, 1, 2, 3, \ldots \}$

Spanish word with the same meaning as *integers*: enteros

To find the **mean** of a set of data, first find the sum of the numbers in the data set and then divide the sum by how many numbers there are in the set.

    Example: Using the set of data as follows: {23, 12, 6, 4, 5, 12, 2, 11, 12, 5, 1, 8, 3}, the sum of the numbers is 104. There are 13 numbers in this set and 104 divided by 13 is 8. Therefore, the *mean* is 8.

Spanish word with the same meaning as *mean*: media

The **median** is the middle data item, where the data are arranged from least to greatest. For a data set with an even number of data items, you add the two middle data values and divide by two to find the median.

    Example: Using this set of data from the preceding example, {23, 12, 6, 4, 5, 12, 2, 11, 12, 5, 1, 8, 3}, first arrange the data in order from least to greatest: {1, 2, 3, 4, 5, 5, 6, 8, 11, 12, 12, 12, 23}. The <u>median</u> is 6, because it is the middle number.

Spanish word with the same meaning as *median*: mediana

Parallel: straight lines or planes that never intersect.

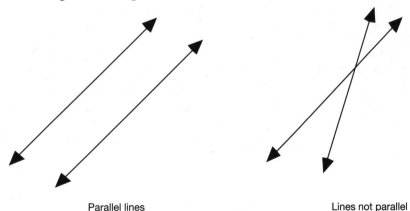

Parallel lines   Lines not parallel

Spanish word with the same meaning as *parallel*: paralelo(a)

A **parallelogram** is a four-sided geometric figure, with each pair of opposite sides being parallel.

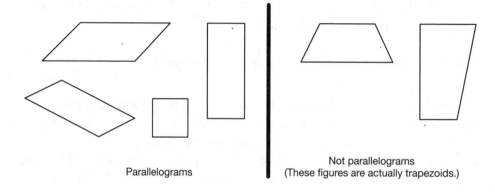

Parallelograms

Not parallelograms
(These figures are actually trapezoids.)

Spanish word with the same meaning as *parallelogram*: paralelograma

The **perimeter** is the distance around any closed, geometric, two-dimensional shape.

Spanish word with the same meaning as *perimeter*: perímetro

A **pie chart** (or **circle graph**) is a way of displaying numerical data by dividing a circle into sectors. Each sector represents a category of the data and the size of each sector represents the relative size of that category compared to the whole. The parts are usually identified as percents of the whole.

Here is a way of showing the breakfast data for Mrs. Garcia's class in a circle graph.

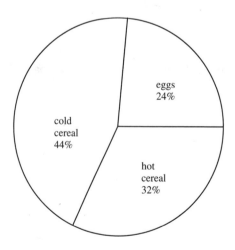

eggs
24%

cold
cereal
44%

hot
cereal
32%

Spanish words with the same meaning as *circle graph*: gráfica circular

A **prime number** is a number that has exactly two factors: itself and 1.

The smallest prime is 2, because only $2 \times 1 = 2$; 7 is a prime number, because only $7 \times 1 = 7$; 9 is *not* a prime number because 9 has three different factors: 1, 3, and 9.

Spanish word(s) with the same meaning as *prime*: primo (número primo)

The **probability** of an event's happening is a number from 0 to 1, which measures the chance of that event happening. The probability of most events is a value between 0 (impossible) and 1 (certain). A probability can be written as a fraction, as a decimal or as a percentage.

Spanish word with the same meaning as *probability*: probabilidad

The **radius** of a circle is the segment that begins at the center of the circle and ends at the circumference. Its length is half the diameter. (See *circle*.)

Spanish word with the same meaning as *radius*: radio

To choose **randomly** from a set means that each item of a set has an equal chance of being chosen. Five marbles of the same shape and size are put in a bag. There is a blue, a red, a white, a black, and a yellow marble in the bag. If you reach into the bag without looking, what is the probability of pulling out a red marble?

Since you are not looking and each of the five marbles feels the same, there is an equal chance of choosing any one of the five marbles. The answer is one out of five or $\frac{1}{5}$.

Spanish word with the same meaning as *randomly*: aleatoriamente

Scatterplot is a two-dimensional graph in which each point stands for two related items. For examples of scatterplots, see *correlation*.

Spanish word with the same meaning as *scatterplot*: dispersograma

Scientific notation is a way of writing numbers as a product of a power of 10 and a number greater than or equal to 1 but less than 10. Scientific notation gives us a way of writing very large numbers or very small numbers. Scientific notation uses powers of 10 to move the decimal point to the right or left.

For example $1.5 \times 10^6 = 1,500,000$ and $1.5 \times 10^{-6} = 0.0000015$

In scientific notation, 8,906,000 is 8.906×10^6 and 0.0000023 is 2.3×10^{-6}.

Spanish words with the same meaning as *scientific notation*: notación científica

Simple interest: When you have a savings account, the bank pays you for the use of your money. This payment is called interest. When the term <u>simple interest</u> is used, it means that the interest is calculated by finding the product of the original amount of money, the interest rate, and the time the money is in the bank.

For example, suppose you put $200 in a bank that pays 8% per year for 1 year. Then the simple interest is $200.00 \bullet 0.08 \bullet 1 = \$48$.

Spanish words with the same meaning as *simple interest*: interés simple

Slope of a line on a graph is the ratio of the change in y-values to the change in x-values between any two points on the line.

Spanish word with the same meaning as *slope*: pendiente

The **square** of a number is the product of a number multiplied by itself. The square of 4 is 16 because $4 \bullet 4$ is 16. To square 13 means to multiply $13 \bullet 13$, which is 169.

The symbol is the exponent ^{2}. $4^2 = 16$ and $13^2 = 169$.

Spanish word with the same meaning as *square*: cuadrado

Square root is the opposite, or undoing, of squaring a number. Because $4^2 = 16$, then the square root of 16 is 4. Because $13^2 = 169$, then the square root of 169 is 13. The symbol for square root is $\sqrt{}$, so $\sqrt{9}$ is 3, because $3^2 = 9$.

Spanish words with the same meaning as *square root*: raíz cuadrada

The **surface area** of a solid is the sum of the areas of all the faces of the solid. If the solid is curved like a cylinder or cone, the surface area can be found by unfolding the surface to make it flat and finding the area of the flat figure.

Spanish words with the same meaning as *surface area*: área de superficie

A **trapezoid** is a geometric figure with four sides where exactly two of the sides are parallel. (see *parallelogram*)

Spanish word with the same meaning as *trapezoid*: trapecio

The **volume** of a figure such as a rectangular solid, cylinder, cone, or sphere is a measure of the amount of space inside the figure. Volume is measured in cubic units. For an example, see the example for standard 7MG2.3 on page 78.

Spanish word with the same meaning as *volume*: volumen

The **x-intercept** is the value of x in an ordered pair that describes where the graph of the line intersects the x-axis. When an x-intercept is written as an ordered pair, a "0" will always be in the second spot because the y-value must be the 0 there. For example, an x-intercept of "5" has the coordinates $(5, 0)$.

Spanish words with the same meaning as *x-intercept*: intercepción x

The **y-intercept** is the value of y in an ordered pair that describes where the graph of the line intersects the y-axis. When a y-intercept is written as an ordered pair, a "0" will always be in the first spot because the x-value must be 0 there. For example, a y-intercept of "5" has the coordinates $(0, 5)$.

Spanish words with the same meaning as *y-intercept*: intercepción y

ANSWER KEY TO THE PRACTICE TEST

Question Number	Standard	Standard	Correct Answer
1	7NS2.5	~	D
2	7NS2.4	~	B
3	7NS1.2	7MR1.2	C
4	7NS1.6	~	B
5	7NS2.1	~	C
6	7NS2.2	~	C
7	7NS1.7	~	A
8	7NS1.3	~	B
9	7NS2.3	~	D
10	7NS1.2	~	B
11	7NS1.1	~	B
12	7PS1.1	~	A
13	6PS3.3	~	B
14	6PS2.5	~	D
15	6PS3.1	~	A
16	6PS1.1	~	B
17	6PS2.5	7MR2.4	B
18	6PS3.5	~	C
19	7PS1.2	~	D
20	7AF1.1	~	C
21	7AF3.3	7MR2.3	A
22	7AF2.2	~	C
23	7AF3.4	~	A
24	7AF4.2	7MR2.1	C
25	7AF4.1	~	C
26	7AF1.2	~	B
27	7AF3.3	~	C
28	7AF3.1	~	B
29	7AF4.2	~	D
30	7AF2.1	~	A
31	7AF1.5	~	B
32	7MG1.2	~	C
33	7MG1.3	7MR1.1	C
34	7MG1.3	~	A
35	7MG2.2	~	C
36	7MG2.4	~	A
37	7MG2.3	~	D
38	7MG3.3	~	B
39	7MG3.2	~	A
40	7MG2.1	~	B
41	7MG1.1	~	A
42	7MG3.4	~	B
43	7MG2.2	7MR3.3	D
44	1A10.0	~	C
45	1A6.0	~	D
46	1A8.0	~	B
47	1A9.0	~	B
48	1A15.0	~	A
49	1A3.0	~	A
50	1A4.0	~	C
51	1A7.0	~	A
52	1A5.0	~	A
53	1A2.0	~	D

Appendix

ANSWER KEYS TO THE ADDITIONAL SAMPLE QUESTIONS

Number Sense Answer Key to Sample Items

Question Number	Standard	Correct Answer
1	7NS1.1	C
2	7NS1.2	C
3	7NS1.3	C
4	7NS1.6	C
5	7NS1.7	C
6	7NS2.3	A
7	7NS2.4	B
8	7NS1.7	C
9	7NS2.5	D

Measurement and Geometry Answer Key to Sample Items

Question Number	Standard	Correct Answer
1	7MG1.1	D
2	7MG1.2	D
3	7MG1.3	B
4	7MG2.1	D
5	7MG2.1	A
6	7MG2.2	B
7	7MG2.3	C
8	7MG3.2	B
9	7MG3.3	B

Statistics, Data Analysis, and Probability Answer Key to Sample Items

Question Number	Standard	Correct Answer
1	6PS2.5	C
2	6PS3.5	C
3	7PS1.1	D
4	7PS1.2	B

Mathematical Reasoning Answer Key to Sample Items

Question Number	Standard	Standard	Correct Answer
1	7MR1.1	7AF4.2	A
2	7MR2.1	7NS1.2	C
3	7MR2.3	7PS1.2	D
4	7MR2.4	7NS1.2	C

Algebra and Functions Answer Key to Sample Items

Question Number	Standard	Correct Answer
1	7AF1.1	D
2	7AF1.5	C
3	7AF2.2	B
4	7AF2.2	D
5	7AF3.3	B
6	7AF4.1	D
7	7AF4.1	A
8	7AF4.2	A

Algebra 1 Answer Key to Sample Items

Question Number	Standard	Correct Answer
1	1A2.0	C
2	1A3.0	A
3	1A4.0	A
4	1A5.0	D
5	1A6.0	A
6	1A8.0	C
7	1A9.0	B
8	1A15.0	A

NOTES

71839-71839 • PDF19

OSP 09 112154
R04-004 403-0005-04 10-04 529M

NOTES

NOTES

NOTES

NOTES

NOTES

NOTES

NOTES

NOTES

NOTES

NOTES

NOTES